TECHNOLOGY UTILIZATION

POTTING
ELECTRONIC MODULES

A REPORT

NATIONAL AERONAUTICS AND SPACE ADMINISTRATION

NASA SP-5077

POTTING ELECTRONIC MODULES

A REPORT

By
R. E. Keith

Prepared under contract for NASA
by Battelle Memorial Institute

Technology Utilization Division
OFFICE OF TECHNOLOGY UTILIZATION   1969
NATIONAL AERONAUTICS AND SPACE ADMINISTRATION
Washington, D.C.

NOTICE • This document was prepared under the sponsorship of the National Aeronautics and Space Administration. Neither the United States Government nor any person acting on behalf of the United States Government assumes any liability resulting from the use of the information contained in this document, or warrants that such use will be free from privately owned rights.

For Sale by the Superintendent of Documents,
U.S. Government Printing Office, Washington, D.C. 20402
Price 35 cents
Library of Congress Catalog Card Number 77–603553

Foreword

To assure the greatest possible benefits to the public from the nation's space program, the engineers and scientists at NASA research centers and contractors continuously screen the emerging technology for innovative ideas, concepts, working processes, methods, tools, etc. Many of these have applications in non-aerospace business and industry. This is one of a series of publications issued by NASA aimed at the goal of transferring space-derived technology to other spheres of activity.

This report reviews major developments in the technology of encapsulation, potting, and embedment of electronic modules, and the materials used in these processes. Because the literature in this field is voluminous, the coverage of material already well summarized in previous reports and studies has been avoided. A list of major books, bibliographies, and reviews on the subject is provided. Emphasis is given to such subjects of current interest in the field as internal stresses in encapsulated modules, and such recently applied processing techniques as transfer molding.

The reader seeking general information on the subject, or a guide to specific sources of information relating to polymers and their use in embedment processes, should find this report useful.

RONALD J. PHILIPS
Director
Technology Utilization Division

Acknowledgments

In addition to the Battelle-Columbus library facilities, the following sources of information were used in the preparation of this report:
- National Aeronautics and Space Administration
- Redstone Scientific Information Center, Huntsville, Ala.
- Defense Documentation Center, Alexandria, Va.
- Electronic Properties Information Center, Culver City, Calif.
- Plastics Technical Evaluation Center, Picatinny Arsenal, Dover, N.J.
- Knowledge Availability Systems Center, University of Pittsburgh, Pittsburgh, Pa.

Messrs. E. N. Baker, H. R. Brewer, J. R. Hoffman, J. M. Knadler III, W. J. Patterson, and B. K. Tannehill of NASA's Marshall Space Flight Center provided valuable and timely information, which is acknowledged with the author's appreciation. The assistance of Battelle coordinators for technology utilization reports, H. R. Batchelder and V. W. Ellzey, is also gratefully acknowledged.

Contents

CHAPTER 1

Introduction

The urgent demand for reliability in electronic circuits and systems for use in spacecraft has led NASA to look anew at existing technologies in many areas of design, materials, and fabricating techniques. Recent developments in the technology of encapsulating, potting, or embedding electronic modules are covered in this report. Most of the information presented deals with modules constructed from discrete components by welding or soldering techniques. Such modules are typically three-dimensional with components stacked like cordwood, or they are planar like printed circuits. The encapsulation of integrated and film-type circuits is mentioned only briefly. Solid resin, foam, and conformal encapsulants are discussed, but only passing references are made to liquid, dry powder, and ceramic encapsulants, because they are seldom used for modules containing active solid-state electronic components.

From the beginnings of the electrical industry, critical circuit components have been coated, buried, or otherwise encased in dielectric materials to isolate them from adverse environmental and operational effects of oxygen, moisture, temperature, electrical flashover and current leakage, mechanical shock, and vibration. The first materials used for this purpose were waxes and asphaltic compounds. Although these substances are still used to some extent, synthetic polymers are now the most widely used electrical encapsulants.

DEFINITIONS

Several terms relating to the technology of encapsulation are loosely used throughout the electrical and electronic industries. Authorities do not agree among themselves in defining some of these terms. The definitions listed below are generally in accord with industrial usage and should be helpful to the reader in understanding the subsequent discussions in this report.

1. Encapsulation—This word is used by some authorities (ref. 1) as the broad, generic term to include any process that totally encloses a circuit or component, except for leads, in a monolithic dielectric. Other authorities use the term in a more restricted sense to refer to the casting or molding of dielectric around a circuit, with the resulting

1

block having a definite shape, usually a simple polyhedron. Another use of the word "encapsulation" not related to electronic packaging, but which is certain to cause increasing confusion in the literature, refers to the enclosure of a liquid or solid chemical in microspheres of gelatin or similar material that can be ruptured at will by heat or pressure.

2. Potting—Potting differs from the restricted definition of encapsulation in that the mold becomes part of the final assembly. It is used particularly with reference to sealing of cable connectors, but also is used when a component, such as a transformer or a resistor, is cast into a preformed metal or plastic case by using a hardening dielectric.

3. Embedment—This term connotes the complete burial of a circuit in a surrounding material. It is also commonly used when the dielectric consists of a granular or powdered dielectric, a foam, or a ceramic.

4. Conformal Coating—This term is used frequently to include any dielectric coating of more or less constant thickness that follows the contour of the circuit assembly, regardless of whether it is applied by dipping, spraying, or brushing. One authority (ref. 2) prefers to call such a coating applied by dipping "encapsulation."

5. Surface Coating—Some authorities use this term to mean a coating that is brushed or sprayed onto a circuit. Others refer to brushed or sprayed coatings simply as conformal coatings.

6. Impregnation—This term has long been used in the electrical apparatus industry to mean the process by which all externally connected air spaces in a component, such as a coil or a motor stator, are filled with a resin. This is most often accomplished by immersing the component in the liquid resin and applying vacuum and/or pressure.

SOURCES OF COMPILED INFORMATION

The reader who is unfamiliar with electronic module embedment will find that available literature (refs. 1 through 3) gives an excellent introduction to the subject as well as helpful discussions of polymer chemistry and typical properties of the different classes of embedment materials. The *Modern Plastics Encyclopedia* (ref. 4), issued annually, contains similar information on properties as well as practical instructions for production molding processes. An extensive summary of manufacturers' data on potting and encapsulating compounds was prepared by American Machine and Foundry, Inc. (ref. 5) in 1961 and serves as an excellent reference to the chemistry and characteristics of such materials up to that year. The entire subject of electronic packaging has been covered in a recent four-volume handbook prepared by the Hughes Aircraft Company (ref. 6).

In addition to the books and handbooks, a number of bibliographies covering various aspects of electronic packaging and embedment (refs. 7 through 15) have appeared since 1960. These bibliographies, most of which are annotated, provide an introduction to the report, journal, and trade literature.

CHAPTER 2

Classes of Embedment Materials

In addition to waxes and asphalts, some electronic components and circuits are embedded in various types of ceramics, including air-drying and heat-curing cements (refs. 16 through 19); in liquids (refs. 20 and 21); and in unbonded granular or powdered solids (refs. 22 and 23). Circuits and apparatus usually embedded in such materials are transformers, high-temperature motors, coils, and passive networks. They seldom include active semiconductor circuits, since the service capabilities of organic resins are adequate for the relatively low upper-operating temperature limit of semiconductors, which is about 85° C. Only organic resin-type embedment materials, many of which are filled with inorganic materials, will be considered further in this report. The reader interested in ceramic, liquid, or powder encapsulating materials is referred to the literature cited above.

Most of the embedment of electronic modules is done today with one of three classes of polymers—epoxy resins, urethanes, or silicones, of which the epoxies are used most frequently. All these materials can be prepared as either continuous solids or foams. They are thermosetting materials; that is, their curing reactions include the cross-linking of molecules. Consequently they are infusible when cured. They will soften somewhat with the application of heat but will degrade by charring before they will melt. In this respect they differ from the general class of thermoplastic polymers.

The particular epoxies, urethanes, and silicones used for electronic module embedment also share two other characteristics that are important to that application. First, these polymers, with the exception of polyurethane foams, are addition-curing rather than condensation-curing. Thus while curing they do not liberate water or an acid that would be harmful to the electronic components. Second, they do not generally contain volatile solvents; they are, therefore, essentially "100-percent solids." Solvent-containing encapsulants shrink excessively during curing, and the solvents may cause swelling or solution of organic materials in the circuitry of the module.

In industry, much of the embedment of electronic components is done with polyesters, diallyl phthalate resins, phenolics, elastomers such as polysulfide rubber, and thermoplastics such as polyethylene.

5

Polystyrene is also used for applications where a low dielectric loss is required. For a variety of reasons, however, these materials are less suitable than epoxies, urethanes, and silicones for encapsulating high-performance aerospace modules. Several brief summaries of embedment materials, which enumerate the advantages and disadvantages of each class, are available (refs. 24 through 26).

EPOXY RESINS

Epoxy resins, most of which are made by combining such materials as bisphenol A with epichlorohydrin, are available from numerous manufacturers in a wide range of polymeric chain lengths and with a variety of substituted groups in the chains. The length of the chains determines the viscosity of the resin and its molecular weight. When the viscosity becomes too high, the resin is no longer pourable and is no longer suitable for casting.

Several classes of curing agents for epoxy materials are available. The anhydrides are effective in producing cured resins having the best high-temperature properties, but they are difficult to use because most of the anhydrides are solid at room temperature. Amine curing agents are most commonly used with epoxies intended for module embedment because they are liquids that can be conveniently mixed with resin and because extremely high heat resistance is not required in solid-state circuits. The particular curing agent employed not only affects the properties of the cured resin, but also influences the rate of curing and the amount of heat liberated during curing. Curing agents must therefore be chosen with careful consideration of the desired pot life and the volume of resin being cured. High exothermic characteristics coupled with large volumes of resin may result in runaway cures.

Properties of the epoxy resins that have led to their wide use include their resistance to chemicals and moisture, good mechanical and electrical properties, low curing shrinkage, dimensional stability, reasonable cost, and ease of use in production. The present state of the epoxy molding technology has recently been reviewed by Delmonte (ref. 27).

URETHANES

Polyurethanes are produced by causing di-isocyanates or poly-isocyanates to react with chemicals containing two or more active hydrogen sites in their molecules. Examples are polyesters, poly-ethers, glycols and other polyhydroxy alcohols (polyols), and water. Although most of the polyurethanes are either flexible or rigid foams and fibers, they can be prepared as solid, pore-free materials. Both solid and foamed polyurethanes are used in the embedment of modules.

Polyurethanes tend to be rubbery, or elastomeric, and have excellent tear strength and resistance to abrasion. The loss of mechanical strength of these materials is quite rapid as service temperature is increased above room temperature. The isocyanates have strong unpleasant odors and may liberate poisonous hydrogen cyanide gas during curing. Consequently they should be used only with adequate ventilation. Manufacturers have largely overcome these disadvantages by packaging the materials in a partially processed form that is convenient to use for the embedment of electronic modules (refs. 28 and 29).

SILICONES

Silicones consist of chains of alternating silicon and oxygen atoms with a variety of carbon-based side groups. In this respect they differ from conventional polymers in which the chains consist almost entirely of carbon atoms. Because of their structure, the silicones are resistant to oxidation, have excellent electrical resistance, and retain their mechanical properties over a wider temperature range than other classes of polymers. In addition to the rigid and elastomeric silicones available for the embedment of modules, there is a silicone gel that can be penetrated by a probe for circuit testing and will then heal itself. The use of silicones for embedment applications has been somewhat limited by their relatively low mechanical strengths, poor adhesion to the underlying circuitry, comparatively high cost, and the unavailability until recently of an addition-curing system. Considerable progress, however, has been made in solving these problems (ref. 30).

HYBRID POLYMERS

The development of new and improved polymers is an active field. Epoxies, urethanes, and silicones can be made to copolymerize with the object of imparting the beneficial properties of each class of resin to the resulting polymers (ref. 31). For high-temperature service, efforts are being made to develop compact, three-dimensional polymers that are either aromatic or heterocyclic and contain at least some silicone (ref. 32). Such compounds as carboranes and polybenzimidazoles are under investigation.

CHAPTER 3

Embedment Systems

A system for embedding electronic modules consists of the basic polymer and its curing agent, and various added materials. The additives may include fillers, flexile materials, coloring agents, flow-control agents, antioxidants, and other materials that will modify the characteristics of the resin/hardener system and bring about desirable results. Most of the additives are compounded by the manufacturer of the embedment system and need not concern the module manufacturer directly. Many of the additives, however, have significant effects on the end properties of the material and, in choosing among possible embedment systems, care must be taken to distinguish between the properties of polymer systems developed by pure or simplified research and those of commercial embedment materials.

FILLERS

From the standpoint of the module manufacturer, fillers are probably the most important additives. Fillers generally modify the basic resin/hardener properties more extensively than the other types of additive and are sometimes added by the user since the principles governing their use require no significant specialized knowledge of polymer chemistry. In module embedment, fillers will nearly always be used, particularly with the more rigid epoxy and silicone resins. The purpose is to obtain a better match between the thermal expansion characteristics of the resin and the circuit components, and to increase the thermal conductivity of the resin.

Bergey, Shanta, and Dalphone (ref. 33) have collected and tabulated thermal and electrical conductivities, expansion coefficients, densities, dielectric properties, and thermal shock resistances of some 78 possible fillers. They have also evaluated the effects of the most promising fillers in various applications. Among the mineral fillers that they and other investigators have evaluated in detail are silica sand, boron nitride, magnesia, mica, zirconium silicate, alumina, and beryllia (refs. 33 through 37). The detailed effects of fillers as well as their specific properties are discussed in Chapter 4.

There are definite limits to the amount of any particular filler that a given resin system will accept without becoming excessively viscous.

In general, it is possible to achieve higher concentrations with granular fillers having controlled particle size than with fillers in the form of fine powders. Fine powdery fillers also tend to make the system thixotropic. (Thixotropic materials are viscous if allowed to stand undisturbed, but decrease in viscosity temporarily following stirring or other agitation. On standing, they revert to their original gelled state.) One method of achieving higher filler concentrations is to place the filler around the module and then infiltrate it with the resin. This approach was used by Baker (ref. 36) with beneficial effects on thermal conductivity.

LOW-DENSITY FILLERS

The addition of mineral fillers usually gives resin systems increased density, which is undesirable for applications in which minimum weight is essential. Fillers of hollow glass, ceramic, plastic spheres, or microballoons give embedment systems reduced densities and are becoming increasingly popular for module embedment. A system in which glass microspheres are used is designated as Type IV in NASA specification MSFC–SPEC–222A. Experimental studies of such systems have been reported by several investigators (refs. 38 through 41).

FOAMS

Embedment materials of minimum density are obtained when the material is in the form of a foam (ref. 42). The urethanes are the most commonly used foams, since their curing reaction can be made to liberate carbon dioxide. Foaming can also be caused to occur in epoxies, silicones, and other resins by adding a blowing (gas evolving) agent. The foaming is done *in situ* in the mold cavity containing the circuit being embedded. Control of the foam's density and rigidity over wide ranges is possible by varying the percentage of the blowing agent and the composition of the resin. The low densities of foams are obtained at the expense of mechanical strengths and moisture resistance.

UNDERCOATS AND OTHER DUPLEX SYSTEMS

To protect circuit components, particularly those encased in glass, from stresses caused by curing of the embedment resin and from mechanical shock in service, a thin, flexible conformal undercoat is sometimes applied to the module circuitry prior to embedment. Silicone rubber or solid polyurethane is usually used as the undercoat material. Recent work has confirmed that the value of undercoating increases in proportion to the rigidity of the outer embedment resin (ref. 43), and that it has little or no beneficial effect when used with flexible epoxy or foamed embedment materials.

An unusual duplex system has been reported that combines repairability, moisture resistance, and light weight (ref. 44). The module is embedded in glass microspheres cemented together with a polyvinyl butyral binder. A thin (0.015 mil) epoxy exterior coating provides the environmental barrier. To repair the module, the epoxy is first cut away. The microspheres can then be flushed clear of the defective component with acetone, which readily dissolves polyvinyl butyral. After the component has been replaced, fresh microspheres can be cemented in place and an outer epoxy patch applied. A limitation of the system would seem to be the relatively low mechanical shock resistance of the closely packed microspheres.

Dunaetz and Tuckerman (ref. 45) have developed a duplex embedment system that they refer to as "egg shell" embedment. It is similar to the system described above except that polyurethane foam, instead of microspheres, is the interior material. The epoxy shell is effective in blocking outgassing of the polyurethane in vacuum.

CHAPTER 4

Properties of Polymeric Embedment Materials

This chapter deals with the mechanical, physical, and electrical properties of encapsulants that are related to their use with electronic modules. The many different formulations and variations that are possible among batches make it impossible to predict the exact properties of any particular batch of a specific manufacturer's product. Nevertheless, the different classes of encapsulants do have properties that fall into certain characteristic ranges.

Drinkard and Snyder (ref. 5) summarized in graphical and tabular form a large quantity of manufacturers' data that became available in June 1961. Their graphs representing those properties for which data were available will be presented later in this chapter. They have been modified to include the maximum and/or minimum property values established by NASA specifications, where appropriate. Where a specification includes different types of materials, these materials are indicated by their identifying Roman numerals that are used in the specifications. In several cases the specification limits fall outside the ranges found by Drinkard and Snyder. Presumably these limits apply to materials developed since 1961, since existing materials are qualified for use under all of the NASA specifications.

TESTING METHODS

It is necessary to understand something of the structure of the chemical industry to appreciate fully the need for continual testing of organic materials purchased for production use. With the exception of silicones, which are manufactured by firms that also compound finished casting and molding materials, the basic resins are usually produced by large, general chemical manufacturers. The embedment material supplier then blends relatively small quantities of these resins with a wide variety of chemicals that serve as fillers, extenders, elastic or flexible agents, moderators, flow-control agents, coloring agents, and the like into proprietary formulations. Since this compounding is usually a batch process, lot-to-lot variations are liable to be significant and, considering the great variety of different chemicals available for use in compounding, no two manufacturers' compounds are likely to be identical in all respects. Stefanski (ref. 46) has discussed the testing requirements involved in the production of plastics from the point of view of manufacturing quality control. Regardless of the care exercised by the manufacturer, however, the user of plastics must maintain his own continual quality check on materials, because they may age and deteriorate in storage.

The American Society for Testing and Materials (ASTM) has established standard test methods for determining many of the properties of encapsulants. These standard tests provide a common basis for comparison, and the properties measured by ASTM procedures should always be included in published articles when they are pertinent. Federal test specifications and military specifications include testing methods for some properties not covered by ASTM. A listing of the more common ASTM, federal, and military specification test methods applicable to encapsulation and embedment systems is given in table I.

Because these tests are often unnecessarily elaborate for screening purposes, the users of plastics have developed a variety of simple, rapid tests, by which those compounds that are clearly unsatisfactory for a given application can be eliminated from consideration. For example, one company evaluates selected embedment resins by potting a castellated nut in a small, but constant quantity of each compound in throwaway aluminum foil pans, and making a visual examination of the cured blocks of plastics to determine their relative cracking sensitivities. Only compounds that pass this test are then subjected to the ASTM tests. There is a danger in using nonstandardized tests, however. It is possible to devise tests that no available material can pass consistently, and judgment is therefore necessary, together with advice from material suppliers, in establishing such in-house tests. In the last analysis, the performance of an encapsulant in the intended application is more meaningful than any of the material tests. For this reason, finished modules should be subjected to appropriate environmental tests that stimulate service conditions as closely as can be economically justified.

MECHANICAL PROPERTIES

A number of mechanical properties affect the selection of an embedment material for a given application. The more important ones discussed in this report include elastic modulus, tensile strength, tear strength, compressive strength, compression set, flexural strength, impact strength, and hardness.

Elastic Modulus

The elastic modulus is the ratio of stress to strain below the propor-

TABLE I.—*Some standard testing specifications applicable to polymeric embedment materials*

Specification	Method	Specification title	Property
		Department of Defense	
MIL-C-3015		Connectors, Electric, "AN" Type	Arc resistance.
MIL-E-5272	Procedure I	Environmental Testing, Aeronautical and Associated Equipment.	Fungus resistance.
MIL-I-16923		Insulating Compounds, Electrical Embedding.	Thermal shock, thermal conductivity.
MIL-R-3065		Rubber, Fabricated Parts	
		General Services Administration	
FED-STD-175	1041.1	Adhesives, Methods of Testing	Peel strength.
FED-STD-406	1011	Plastics, Methods of Testing	Tensile specimen preparation.
	1082		Hardness.
	2031		Coefficient of thermal expansion.
	2051		Brittleness temperature.
	4021		Dielectric constant, dissipation factor.
	4041		Insulation resistance.
	6011		Temperature resistance.
FED-STD-601	3021	Rubber, Sampling and Testing	Hardness.
	3311		Compression set.
	4111		Tensile strength.
	4121		Elongation.
	4211		Tear resistance.
	8031		Peel strength.
	14011		Specific gravity, viscosity.

TABLE I.—*Some standard testing specifications applicable to polymeric embedment materials*—Continued

Specification	Specification title	Property
National Aeronautics and Space Administration		
MSFC-SPEC-202A	Compound, Potting and Molding, Elastomeric--	Insulation resistance, high potential, low temperature flexibility, electrical resistance at 100° C, moisture resistance, shrinkage, ozone resistance, nonvolatile content, storage life, application life, viscosity, adhesion.*
MSFC-SPEC-222B	Resin Compounds, Electrical and Environmental Insulation, Epoxy.	Insulation resistance, high potential moisture resistance, thermal conductivity, nonvolatile content, application life, shrinkage, viscosity.*
MSFC-SPEC-379A	Compounds, Potting and Encapsulating, Silicone-	Ozone resistance, water absorption, low-temperature flexibility, shrinkage, humid electrical resistance, storage life, application life.*
MSFC-SPEC-393A	Compound, Printed Circuit Board, Conformal Coating, Elastomeric.	Sprayability, volume, and surface resistivity, insulation resistance, high potential resistance at 121° C, humid electrical resistance, shrinkage, storage life, application life, nonvolatile content, adhesion.*
MSFC-SPEC-418	Polyurethane Foams for Electronic Equipment--	Aging stability, volume change, storage life.*

*Tests described in addition to standard tests referenced to MIL, FED, or ASTM specifications.

TABLE I.—*Some standard testing specifications applicable to polymeric embedment materials*—Continued

Specification	Specification title and property
	American Society for Testing and Materials
D 149	Test for Dielectric Breakdown Voltage and Dielectric Strength of Electrical Insulating Materials at Commercial Power Frequencies.
D 150	Test for a-c Capacitance, Dielectric Constant, and Loss Characteristics of Electrical Insulating Materials.
D 256	Test for Impact Resistance of Plastics and Electrical Insulating Materials.
D 257	Test for Electrical Resistance of Insulating Materials.
D 395	Compression Set of Vulcanized Rubber.
D 495	Test for High-Voltage, Low-Current Arc Resistance of Solid Electrical Insulating Materials.
D 570	Test for Water Absorption of Plastics.
D 696	Test for Coefficient of Linear Thermal Expansion of Plastics.
D 746	Method of Test for Brittleness Temperature of Plastics and Elastomers by Impact.
D 792	Test for Specific Gravity and Density of Plastics.
D 1621	Method of Test for Compressive Strength of Rigid Cellular Plastics.
D 1622	Method of Test for Apparant Density of Rigid Cellular Plastics.
D 1692	Method of Test for Flammability of Plastic Foams and Sheeting.
D 2127	Water Absorption of Rigid Cellular Plastics.

tional or elastic limit of the material. The elastic modulus may also be known as the modulus of elasticity, tensile modulus, or Young's modulus. Used in combination with the thermal expansion coefficient, the elastic modulus makes possible the calculation of stress in the encapsulant and of the force that may be imposed on electrical components under thermal cycling.

When pulled in tension, the rigid embedment materials will initially show a nearly linear relation between stress and strain. When the linear portion of the stress-strain curve is exceeded, the material may fall into a zone of plastic flow; that is, the material will continue to deform without appreciable increase in stress until a rupture occurs. Brittle materials, however, may rupture before any substantial plastic flow occurs.

The elastomers, such as the silicone rubbers and elastomeric polyurethanes, have stress-strain curves with a very low initial slope, indicating a very low elastic modulus. The slope of the curves increases continuously with increasing load all the way to rupture. The stress-strain curve shows no noticeable break under increasing load. Because of this low initial elastic modulus, the elastomers do not have the rigidity required for use in "high g" applications (ref. 39).

Care should be taken in selecting resins for applications at low temperatures because of the increase in the modulus of elasticity that takes place below the glass-transition temperature in polymers. Published data on this subject are scant, but Nikolaychik (ref. 47) has shown the variations in the elastic modulus as a function of temperature for a number of epoxies. Graphs from this work are shown in figures 1 through 4.[1] These graphs show significantly higher elastic moduli as temperatures decrease. This phenomenon could lead to increased internal stresses in the embedment materials, and increased forces acting on the enclosed components during expansion and contraction of the materials at low temperatures.

Tensile Strength

The tensile strength of a material is the greatest longitudinal stress (as pounds per square inch) it can bear without rupture or break. The tensile strength is of little direct importance in embedment applications if the strength of the material is sufficient to support the load applied in service. It is, however, an important indicator of the characteristics of a material when it is considered in conjunction with other properties of the material.

Figure 5 shows ranges of typical tensile-strength values for the

---

[1] Stycast and Hysol are trade names of commercial embedment materials.

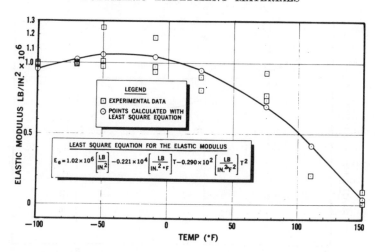

FIGURE 1.—Elastic modulus versus temperature for Hysol 4215. (Used by permission of the Society of Automotive Engineers.)

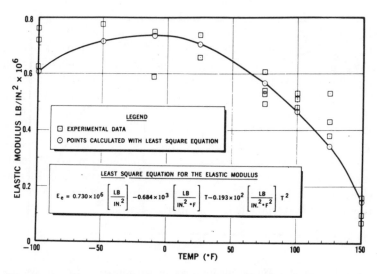

FIGURE 2.—Elastic modulus versus temperature for Stycast 1090. (Used by permission of the Society of Automotive Engineers.)

common embedment materials (ref. 5). The minimum tensile strengths established by applicable NASA specifications for silicones and polyurethanes are also shown. The range of strengths of the polyurethanes has been extended to include the data presented by Harper (ref. 3), and by the Sperry Utah Company (ref. 48). The tensile strengths of foamed materials may range downward to very low strengths at low

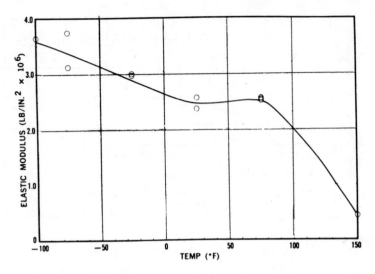

FIGURE 3.—Elastic modulus versus temperature for Stycast 2850 F. (Used by permission of the Society of Automotive Engineers.)

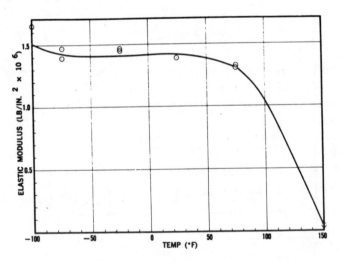

FIGURE 4.—Elastic modulus versus temperature for Stycast 2651. (Used by permission of the Society of Automotive Engineers.)

foam densities. Typical tensile strengths of Eccofoam[2] FPH at room temperature, for example, range from 141 to 200 psi (ref. 49).

Exposures to high temperature and vacuum were found to affect

---

[2] Eccofoam is the trade name of a series of commercially available embedment materials.

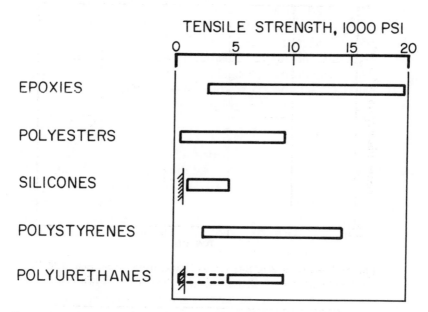

FIGURE 5.—Ranges of typical tensile strengths of cured embedment materials.

the tensile strength properties of both Stycast 1090 epoxy and Ecco-foam FP and FPH polyurethane foams (ref. 49). Increasing the temperature from 70° to 300° F caused a loss of over 90 percent of the tensile strength of Stycast 1090 that was cured using two different curing cycles. The polyurethane foams also lost strength with temperature increases from 70° to 165° F. The tensile strength of Ecco-foam FP dropped from 144 to less than 1 psi, and that of the high-temperature foam, Eccofoam FPH, dropped from 166 to 157 psi. Tensile strengths of Stycast 1090 at room-temperature and 300° F also dropped slightly during exposure to vacuum. The tensile strengths of Eccofoam FP and FPH polyurethane foams, however, increased significantly during vacuum exposure. The data developed by Harper (ref. 2) indicate that the tensile strengths of epoxy materials are reduced when low-density fillers are added.

Tear Strength

The tear strength or tear resistance is a measure of the resistance of such elastomeric materials as the urethanes to the propagation of a crack. The maximum load a block of material can bear without tearing divided by the average thickness of the block is the tear resistance of the material; it is expressed in pounds per inch of thickness.

The tear strength, like the tensile strength, is not of direct use in the selection of an embedment material for a given application. It is a guideline, however, for predicting the behavior of a material in cases where sharp notches may exist in the module. The tear resistance must be sufficient during mechanical loading to prevent damage to the embedment material. Tear strengths of solid polyurethane materials have been reported to vary from 82 to 302 lb/in. (ref. 47).

Compressive Strength

The compressive strength of a material is the maximum compressive stress (the maximum compressive load divided by the minimum area exposed to the load) that can be carried by a test specimen during a compression test. It may or may not be the compressive stress carried by the specimen at the instant of rupture. The measure of compressive strength is of little importance in the process of encapsulation, but it is a useful indicator of material characteristics when viewed in conjunction with other properties. Compressive strength is commonly measured for the rigid embedment materials. The compressive properties of the flexible materials are generally characterized by the compression set, which will be discussed below. The compressive strength, like the tensile strength, of Stycast 1090 is reduced by increased temperatures (ref. 48). It is, however, consistently much higher than the tensile strength of the material.

The compressive strengths of Eccofoam FP and FPH polyurethane foams tend to be lower than the tensile strength under corresponding test conditions. The strength values of the FPH foam are consistently higher than those of the FP foam. Holzbauer and Holbrook (ref. 50) showed the variation of compressive strength with density for two foam-in-place materials. These data, in table II, show an increase in compressive strength with increased density, and also indicate the relative insensitivity of these foam materials to the test direction. Very little differences in strength and no consistent trends are evident in the compressive strengths of the materials when they were tested parallel or perpendicular to the direction of foaming.

The effects of granular fillers on the compressive strengths of epoxies hardened by three different hardening systems have been established (ref. 35). The investigators used the maximum amount of each filler they could add to each resin/hardener system and still retain pourability. The mica-filled systems had approximately the same compressive strengths as the unfilled systems, and silica, zirconium silicate, and hydrated alumina had consistently higher compressive strengths than the unfilled systems. Young (ref. 39) demonstrated that the addition of Eccospheres (a series of commercial hollow spheres made from glass, ceramic, plastic, or metal) to epoxy

TABLE II.—*Compressive strength test results of Stafoam 600† and CPR 23† foam-in-place materials*

	Density (lb/ft³)					
	4		8		20	
	‖* (psi)	⊥** (psi)	‖ (psi)	⊥ (psi)	‖ (psi)	⊥ (psi)
Stafoam 600_____	73	74	159	156	1250	1297
CPR 23_____	67	60	230	251	652	691

*‖ = parallel to the direction of foaming.
** ⊥ = perpendicular to the direction of foaming.
†Stafoam 600 and CPR 23 are trade names of commercial embedment materials.

resins would not affect the compressive yield strength of the resin until the formulation became too viscous to be used for electronic embedding. He also demonstrated that the compressive yield strength of Stycast 1090 increased when the activator content was decreased. The compressive yield strength increased with decreasing amounts of activator until a mixture containing as little as 8 parts (by weight) of activator per 100 parts of resin was attained. The optimum amount of activator that could be used was not established.

Compression Set

Compression set, a characteristic value of the flexible embedment materials, is the residual decrease in thickness of a material measured 30 minutes after its removal from a loading device in which it had been compressively deformed for a definite time and under specified conditions of load and temperature. Compression set is usually expressed as a percentage of the original thickness. Typical ranges of compression set for silicone and polyurethane materials are from 15 to 60 percent, and from 21 to 41 percent respectively (ref. 3).

Flexural Strength

The flexural strength is the ultimate or breaking strength of a material calculated as if the stress in tension or compression increased linearly from zero at the neutral axis to a maximum in the extreme outside fibers (ref. 1). In plastics, this variation is far from linear, and such properties are of interest mainly in structural uses. This test is generally applied to rigid and semirigid materials. The flexural strength cannot be determined for those materials that do not break or that do not fail in the outer fibers. The flexural strength, like the tensile and compressive strengths, is used only as a compositive indicator of material properties for encapsulation applications. Harper (ref. 3) has recorded flexural strength ranges for mineral-filled silicone of from 7000 to 8000 psi. A glass-fiber filled silicone system showed a flexural strength range of from 10 000 to 14 000 psi. This indicates that the type of filler employed affects the flexural strength.

Impact Strength

The impact strength, generally measured by the Izod impact test, is expressed in terms of the energy required to break a notched specimen by a standard impact blow. The impact strength of plastic materials is generally expressed as foot-pounds per inch of specimen width. The Izod value is useful in comparing various types or grades of plastics. Low-impact test results may indicate the need for avoiding sharp internal or external corners in dynamically loaded parts prepared from materials which show notch sensitivity.

The ranges of typical impact-strength values for the common encapsulating materials are shown in figure 6. Also indicated on the figure are the NASA specification requirements for the epoxy materials. The applicable NASA specifications for silicone and polyurethane materials do not require an impact test. The analogous test for the elastomeric materials is the tear test described previously.

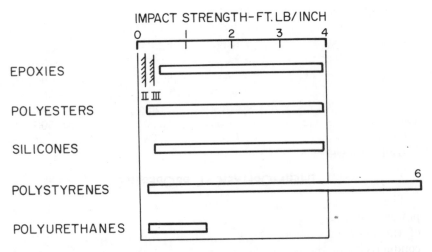

FIGURE 6.—Ranges of typical impact strengths of cured embedment materials.

Hardness

Hardness is a complex property related very closely in practice to the modulus of elasticity, yield strength, and the other structural properties, though the theoretical relationships among them are not clear. Tests of many of the mechanical properties discussed previously may require special specimens or specialized equipment, and thus do not lend themselves to production checks on finished encapsulations. There are simple and widely accepted methods for determining hardness, however. These can be used on finished products without significant damage to either their function or appearance. Such tests can be done on a routine basis to indicate quickly those products that are substandard in formulation or cure and to establish limits of acceptability.

The Rockwell tester, widely used for metals, is effective for testing rigid or relatively hard plastic parts, working with a scale suited to their lower level of hardness. For flexible or soft materials, the Shore Durometer is a recognized standard. These instruments measure the relation between depth of penetration and load for specific conditions, with larger numbers indicating harder materials. Harper (ref. 3) shows typical Shore A hardness ranges for silicone and polyurethane materials respectively of from 20 to 90 (NASA specification limits are from 10 to 60) and 55 to 100 (NASA specification limits are from 45 to 99). The manufacturers' data presented by Drinkard and Snyder (ref. 5) suggest that most of the silicone materials fall in the lower portion of this range, that is, Shore A 30 to 60. Typical hardnesses for epoxy resins range from 80 to 120 Rockwell M (refs. 2 and 5). The addition of low-density fillers did not affect the hardness of Epon 828 epoxy resin after curing (ref. 2).

Christensen (ref. 51) found that a room-temperature-curing silicone material increased in hardness after approximately 1000 hours exposure at 250° C. The material retained good electrical properties, however. The same author reported that a silicone gel became hard and friable after 2000 to 3000 hours exposure at 200° C. McDonnell Aircraft (ref. 52) reported some hardening and shrinkage of EC 1663, a commercial silicone embedment material, after 1000 hours at 500° F (260° C). Another commercial material, RTV 60, suffered a slight loss of hardness after the same exposure.

THERMOPHYSICAL PROPERTIES

The heat generated in encapsulated electronic units, even at modest power levels, may raise operating temperatures considerably because of the close packing of the heat sources and the limited thermal conductivity of the encapsulating material. The demands for greater power from smaller packages, common in military applications, require higher service temperature of all components including encapsulants. The thermophysical properties most affecting the serviceability of an encapsulating material for a given application are thermal expansion, thermal conductivity, and heat-deflection temperature.

Thermal Expansion

The coefficient of thermal expansion is important in determining the stress on the components within an embedment during thermal cycling. Embedding materials generally have somewhat higher coefficients of thermal expansion than those of glasses or metals. This is shown in figure 7, in which the thermal coefficients of expansion of a filled and an unfilled epoxy resin are compared with those of several other materials (ref. 53). These data are within the ranges shown by Drinkard and Snyder in figure 8, upon which the requirements of the applicable NASA specifications for epoxy and silicone materials have been super-imposed. Fillers have a marked effect on the coefficients of thermal expansion of the embedding resin systems, resulting

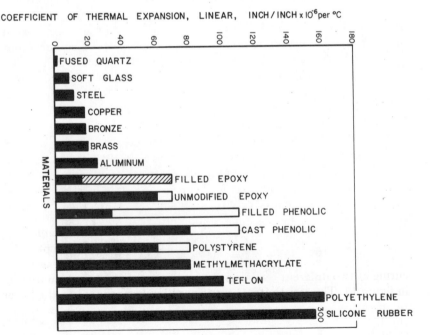

FIGURE 7.—Coefficients of thermal expansion for filled and unfilled epoxy resins compared to those of several other materials. (Used by permission of *Electronic Production and Packaging*.)

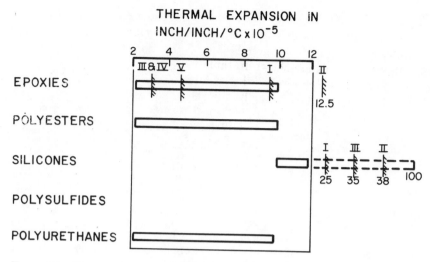

FIGURE 8.—Ranges of typical coefficients of thermal expansion of cured embedment materials.

in the wide ranges shown in figure 8. The coefficients of thermal expansion of epoxy resin systems can be greatly reduced by the addition of inorganic fillers (ref. 35). In general, the coefficient of expansion will depend on the original coefficient of the unfilled resin, the filler material used, and the concentration of the filler. This is true for resins other than epoxies (ref. 53). The silicones usually have much higher coefficients of expansion than the urethanes or epoxies.

The variation in coefficient of thermal expansion with temperature was studied by Nikolaychik (ref. 47) for four commercial epoxy encapsulants. The variations between −100 and 150° F were nearly linear. The equations derived from this study are shown in table III. The coefficient of thermal expansion of Stycast 1090 cured at room temperature was generally reduced by exposure to vacuum at temperatures in the range of −40 to +70° F (ref. 49). In the range of 70 to 300° F, slightly increased expansion coefficients were noted during and after exposure to vacuum.

The coefficient of thermal expansion of urethane foams increases with increasing foam density. In the range of −30 to 30° C, for example, the coefficient of expansion increases from 2.48 C^{-1} for a 2 lb/ft³ foam to 9.25 C^{-1} for a 16 lb/ft³ foam (ref. 42).

Thermal Conductivity

The thermal conductivity of an embedding material is important primarily because of its effect on the amount of heat which can be transferred from the package to the atmosphere or heat sink. Thermal

TABLE III.—*Variations of coefficient of thermal expansion and elastic modulus as a function of temperature for four commercial epoxy encapsulants* (used by permission of the Society of Automotive Engineers)

Name of epoxy	Elastic modulus $E_e \left(\dfrac{lb}{in.^2}\right)$ as a function of temperature, T $(-100°F \leqq T \leqq 150°F)$	Coefficient of thermal expansion $\epsilon_e \left(\dfrac{in.}{in.°F.}\right)$ as a function of temperature, T $(-100°F \leqq T \leqq 150°F)$	Second order transition temperature, Tg (°F)	Average experimental thermal stress index $\left(\dfrac{lb}{°F}\right)$
Hysol 4215	$E_e = 1.02 \times 10^6$ $-0.221 \times 10^4 T$ $-0.290 \times 10^2 T^2$	$\epsilon_e = 24.9 \times 10^{-6}$ $+3.14 \times 10^{-8} T$	50	0. 409
Stycast 1090	$E_e = 0.730 \times 10^6$ $-0.684 \times 10^3 T$ $-0.193 \times 10^2 T^2$	$\epsilon_e = 19.7 \times 10^{-6}$ $+1.99 \times 10^{-8} T$	50	0. 255
Stycast 2850GT	-----------------	$\epsilon_e = 11.7 \times 10^{-6}$ $+8.00 \times 10^{-8} T$	125	0. 163
Stycast 2651	----------------------	$\epsilon_e = 20.5 \times 10^{-6}$ $+13.5 \times 10^{-8} T$	75	0. 316

dissipation is important in keeping the operating temperature of critical components as low as possible. Figure 9 shows the ranges of typical values of thermal conductivity found in the common encapsulating materials by Drinkard and Snyder (ref. 5). Harper (ref. 2) reports that the thermal conductivities of silica-filled epoxy resins varied from 10 to 20 Cal/sec/cm²/°C/cm.

Unfilled epoxy casting resins usually have only minor variations in thermal conductivity. Compounds of high thermal conductivity may be formulated by combining fillers of various types with the resins. Factors other than the thermal conductivity of the filler material are also important in determining the conductivity of a filled encapsulating system. The type, size, and distribution by size of the particles are important variables. The volume concentration of a filler, for example, is more meaningful than its weight concentration in determining the extent to which thermal conductivity can be increased (ref. 34). Typical conductivities obtained by filling epoxy systems are as follows: 72 percent by weight of alumina in Epon 828 yields 31.8 x 10^{-4} Cal/sec/cm²/°C/cm, and 60 percent BeO by weight in Dow 2673.6 resin yields 33.1 x 10^{-9} Cal/sec/cm²/°C/cm (ref. 54). These materials were premixed. Baker reports that by preplacing the filler and im-

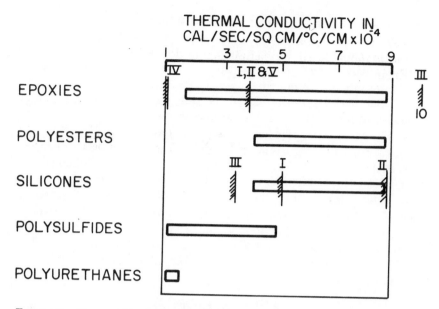

FIGURE 9.—Ranges of typical values of thermal conductivity of cured embedment materials.

pregnating it with resin, he achieved a material with a thermal conductivity of 41.3 x 10^{-4} Cal/sec/cm²/°C/cm (ref. 36). Bergey, Shanta, and Dalphone reported that the maximum thermal conductivity of epoxy resins with sufficient pourability they could obtain was about 22 x 10^{-4} Cal/sec/cm²/°C/cm (ref. 33).

Little change was noted in the thermal conductivity of Stycast 1090 during and after its exposure to vacuum (ref. 49). Two curing cycles were evaluated. One anomaly was noted in material cured at 212° F. Although the thermal conductivity of the material did not change appreciably between 70 and 300° F in vacuum, it dropped from 4.27 x 10^{-4} Cal/sec/cm²/°C/cm to 0.6 x 10^{-4} Cal/sec/cm²/°C/cm after exposure to the vacuum for 24 hours at 70° F. The same material showed little difference in conductivity in the −40 to 70° F range after 24 hours in vacuum at 70° or in either temperature range after 24 hours in vacuum at −40 and +300° F. Little change was noted in the thermal conductivities of Eccofoam FP and FPH urethane foams during or after their exposure to vacuum (ref. 49).

Heat-Deflection Temperature

The heat-deflection temperature, which is of great importance in structural applications, is the temperature at which a specified deflection of a material under specified load and time conditions occurs.

Standard tests, such as the Vicat indentation test, are available to measure the softening temperature. Heat-deflection temperatures of most thermosetting plastics are above the maximum temperature limits of embedment materials that can be tolerated by the semiconductor circuit components.

Another useful criterion for determining the serviceability of an embedment material at elevated temperatures is its maximum operating, or safe-use, temperature. This is frequently expressed as the temperature which a material will withstand without obvious degradation, such as gross distortion, gassing, or charring. The silicones are particularly noted for their capacity to withstand higher temperatures than other classes of polymers. The RTV silicones have typical operating-temperature ranges of from -65 to $600°$ F (ref. 55); however, their tolerance of $600°$ F is limited in time. Typical operating temperature ranges for the epoxy materials are from -65 to $400°$ F. The maximum operating temperature of polyurethane materials is about $300°$ F.

ELECTRICAL PROPERTIES

The electrical characteristics or the physical properties affecting electrical characteristics of an encapsulating material are of major importance in its selection. Dielectric strength, dielectric constant, dissipation factor, arc resistance, and electrical resistivities of commonly used encapsulating materials are discussed below.

Dielectric Strength

Dielectric strength is a measure of the electrical potential gradient the material will withstand without allowing a substantial flow of current. Expressed in volts per mil, the dielectric strength is a measure of the electrical strength of the material as an insulator. High dielectric strengths are desirable in encapsulating materials.

Figure 10 shows dielectric strengths of common encapsulating materials which were compiled by Drinkard and Snyder (ref. 5), and the minimum dielectric strengths required by applicable NASA specifications. Significant improvements in the dielectric strengths of silicone and polyurethane materials have been achieved in recent years.

The dielectric strength of Stycast 1090 was changed by the curing cycle (ref. 49). When it was cured 2 hours at $212°$ F, this material had significantly higher dielectric strength than the same material cured at room temperature; in a vacuum, however, the material cured at room temperature increased slightly in dielectric strength. Polyurethane foams have dielectric strengths somewhat lower than those of the solid encapsulating compounds. Reported values for poly-

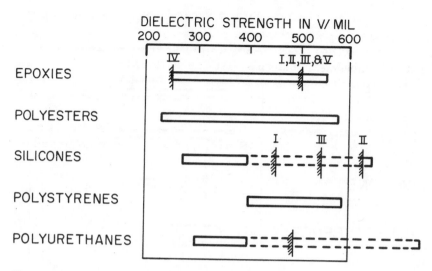

FIGURE 10.—Ranges of typical dielectric strengths of cured embedment materials.

urethane foams range from 44 to 60 volts/mil (ref. 47) to 110 to 150 volts/mil (ref. 42). In general, the dielectric strength of epoxy, silicone, and urethane encapsulating materials drops as temperature increases.

Dielectric Constant

The dielectric constant of a material is the ratio of the capacitance of a capacitor containing the material to the capacitance of the same component with air replacing the material under test as the dielectric. In general, low values of dielectric constant are best for high frequency or power applications in which low power losses are desirable.

Figure 11 shows the ranges of typical dielectric constants of various encapsulating materials available about 1960 (ref. 5). The maximum values allowable under applicable NASA specifications are indicated by the limiting marks. The range shown for the polyurethanes is also typical for solid materials. Foamed polyurethanes have lower dielectric constants, in the range of 1 to 2 (refs. 5 and 39).

In most insulating materials, the dielectric constant increases with temperature, especially at temperatures above a critical temperature of each material. This was observed in filled and unfilled epoxy systems as the heat-deflection temperatures were approached or exceeded and distortion of the material occurred (ref. 35). The dielectric strengths of the epoxy systems at temperatures below the heat-deflection point, however, were affected in various ways by the addition of fillers. Mica and zirconium silicate tended to increase substantially the dielectric constant of the systems in which they were employed.

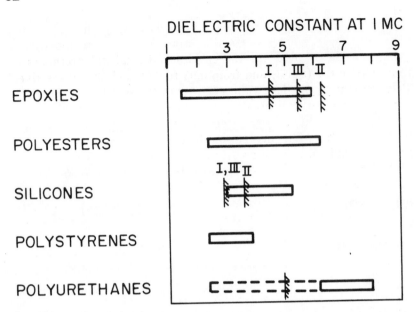

FIGURE 11.—Ranges of typical values of dielectric constants of cured embedment materials.

The effect was more pronounced in the more highly filled systems. Silicone embedment materials had little change in their dielectric constants after 6000-hour exposures to their maximum operating temperatures (ref. 51).

The dielectric constant is also a strong function of frequency, and it varies for each material. In general, the dielectric constant of both filled and unfilled epoxy systems decreases at the higher frequencies (refs. 3 and 35).

Dissipation Factor

The power factor is the ratio of the power dissipated (watts) in an insulating material to the product of the effective voltage and current (volt-ampere) input. It is a measure of the relative dielectric loss in the insulation when the system acts as a capacitor. The power factor is dimensionless and is commonly used in measuring the quality of insulation. The dissipation factor is the tangent of the dielectric-loss angle. Because of the low-loss values ordinarily encountered in insulation, the dissipation factor is practically the equivalent of the power factor, and the terms are used interchangeably (ref. 56). Low values of dissipation factor are favorable, indicating an efficient system with low power losses.

The silicone materials generally have lower dissipation factors than the epoxies and solid polyurethanes under similar conditions. Typical dissipation factors for silicone materials are from 0.001 to 0.01 (ref. 5). Ranges of these values for the epoxies and solid polyurethanes are from 0.01 to 0.1 (ref. 3) and from 0.03 to 0.08 (ref. 56), respectively. Polyurethane foams have values similar to those of the silicones.

Slight temperature increases and short-time exposures to vacuum have little effect on the dissipation factors of epoxies and polyurethane foams (ref. 49). The dissipation factors of filled epoxy systems, however, tend to increase greatly at temperatures near or above the heat-distortion point (heat-deflection temperatures) (ref. 35). Silicone rubber cured at room temperature retains its low dissipation factor during long-time exposures at 250° C, but it becomes hard after approximately 1000 hours at this temperature (ref. 51).

Arc Resistance

The arc resistance is a measure of an electrical breakdown along an insulating surface, caused by the formation of a conductive path on the surface. The extent to which a surface breakdown occurs varies widely among different plastics. Arc resistance is measured in the time (seconds) required for breakdown along the surface of the material being measured under standard conditions. Once arcing has taken place along the surface of many plastics, a carbonized track having relatively low resistance is left behind; consequently, resistance to subsequent arcing is lowered. Surface breakdown is also affected by surface cleanliness and dryness. High values of arc resistance indicate greater resistance to breakdown along the surface and are desirable.

The arc resistance of epoxy resins has been improved by incorporating silica, mica, zirconium-silicate, or hydrated-aluminum fillers (ref. 35). Typical arc-resistance values for filled epoxy systems are in the range of 120 to 300 sec (ref. 3). Typical ranges reported for glass- and mineral-filled silicone systems are 150 to 250 sec and 250 to 420 sec, respectively (ref. 56).

Electrical Resistivity

One of the measures of electrical resistivity is the volume resistivity, which is the electrical resistance between opposite faces of a cube of a given material at a given temperature (ref. 57). The volume resistivity is expressed in ohm-cm; it is not the resistance per unit volume (ohm/cm^3), although this term is sometimes erroneously used. A second measure of the electrical resistance is surface resistivity. The surface resistivity is the resistance between two opposite edges of a surface film 1 cm square. Since such a film is essentially two-dimensional, the units of surface resistivity are actually ohms. To avoid confusion with usual resistance values, however, surface resistivity is sometimes expressed as ohms/cm^2.

The effects of increasing temperature on the volume-resistivity properties of common encapsulating materials are shown in table IV. In contrast to the behavior of metals, the volume resistivity of all of these materials decreases as the temperatures increase. The silicones, however, retain their properties much better than the epoxies and polyurethanes. Short-time exposures to vacuum do not significantly affect either the volume- or surface-resistivity properties of epoxy, silicone, and polyurethane materials (ref. 49).

TABLE IV.—*Temperature effects on volume resistivity properties of electrical encapsulation materials (resistivity in ohm-cm)* [1]

| Material | Test temperature, ° F | | | |
	70	200	300	600
Stycast 1090 [2]	3.8×10^{13}	------------	1.9×10^9	
(Epoxy)	5.1×10^{13}	------------	6.5×10^9	
(ref. 49)				
EC 1663 [3]	6×10^{12}	6×10^{12}	3×10^{12}	1×10^{12}
(Silicone)	7×10^{12}	8×10^{12}	5×10^{12}	2×10^{12}
(ref. 57)				
PR 1525 [3]	5×10^{11}	2×10^{10}	3×10^9	
(Polyurethane)	5×10^{12}	8×10^{11}	4×10^{10}	
(ref. 57)				
Eccofoam FPH [2]	2.9×10^{14}	------------	7×10^{10}	
(Polyurethane foam)	3.2×10^{14}	------------	8×10^{10}	
(ref. 49)				

[1] All tests conducted in accordance with ASTM Specification D257.
[2] Range covers properties of two cure cycles.
[3] Range covers properties of three cure cycles.

The effect of increasing temperature on the surface resistivity of representative encapsulating materials is shown in table V. The variations in surface resistivities with increasing temperature parallel those of the volume resistivities. The silicones retain their surface resistance much better than the epoxies and the polyurethanes.

Humidity adversely affects the electrical resistance of the common encapsulating materials. This is exemplified in figure 12 by the drop in surface resistivity of filled and unfilled epoxy resins as the humidity increases (ref. 56). When tests are being made on a specimen that has been subjected to moist or humid conditions, it is important that measurements are made at controlled time intervals during and after

TABLE V.—*Temperature effects on surface resistivity properties of electrical encapsulation materials (resistivity in ohm/cm)* [1]

Material	Test temperature, ° F			
	70	200	300	600
Stycast 1090 [2] (Epoxy) (ref. 49)	5×10^{13} 2×10^{14}	------------ ------------	6×10^{9} 3×10^{10}	
EC 1663 [3] (Silicone) (ref. 57)	1×10^{12} 2×10^{12}	1×10^{12} 2×10^{12}	9×10^{11} 2×10^{12}	5×10^{11} 8×10^{11}
PR 1525 [3] (Polyurethane) (ref. 57)	8×10^{11} 2×10^{12}	3×10^{11} 1×10^{12}	2×10^{10} 3×10^{11}	
Eccofoam FPH [2] Polyurethane Foam) (ref. 49)	4×10^{14} 5×10^{14}	------------ ------------	8×10^{10} 10×10^{10}	

[1] All tests conducted in accordance with ASTM Specification D257.
[2] Ranges cover properties of two different cure cycles.
[3] Ranges cover properties of three different cure cycles.

the test condition has been applied, since dry-out and resistance of the material can increase rapidly. Other conditions that affect the resistance properties of the materials are moisture content of the specimen, the amount of the applied voltage, and the time during which the voltage is applied.

Measurements of resistivity have been used in studies to determine reaction rates and the extent of cure in polymers, and to detect polymer decomposition (ref. 58). A simple correlation usually exists between resistivity and reaction time. In most circumstances, when such variables as moisture content are controlled, the change in resistivity of a thermosetting material during cure is a useful index of the degree of polymerization. A given value of resistivity cannot be associated with a particular degree of curing, however, except at a specified cure temperature. Plots of resistivity during the process of curing at two different temperatures may cross as shown schematically in figure 13. The resistivity of the "cured" polymer cured at the lower temperature may thus be lower than that of the material cured at the higher temperature. Resistivity measurements are also effective in detecting decomposition resulting from oxidation and heat aging. Thus resistivity measurements can be useful in the study of polymer stability.

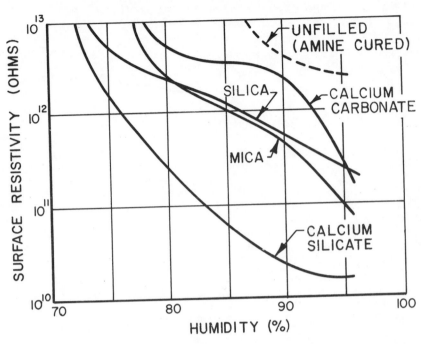

FIGURE 12.—Effect of humidity on surface resistivity of filled and unfilled epoxy resins at 35° C. (Used by permission of *Machine Design*.)

PROCESSING PROPERTIES

In the previous sections, the intrinsic properties of embedment materials that make them applicable and serviceable have been discussed. To be useful, however, both the embedment materials and the module circuitry must withstand the embedding process. The properties of these materials that are essential to successful fabrication of embedded electronic modules are pot life, flow and viscosity, exotherm, and curing shrinkage.

Pot Life

Resins themselves are usually stable in storage indefinitely. In two-part casting systems, hardeners are mixed with the resin just before use. Transfer molding compounds, on the other hand, are quasi-solid mixtures of resins and hardeners that react very slowly at room temperature; consequently, they have limited storage life. The polymerization reaction ordinarily begins at a slow rate immediately when the ingredients are mixed. As the reaction proceeds, the viscosity increases and the mix finally solidifies. The elapsed time between the

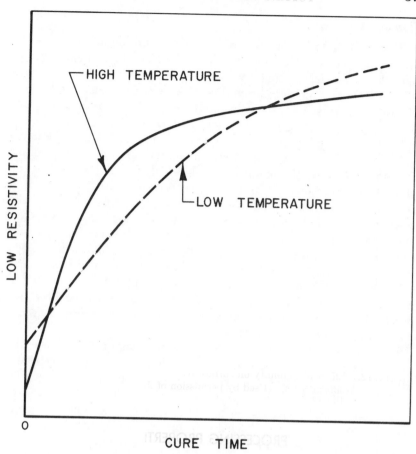

FIGURE 13.—Dependence of the volume resistivity during cure on the cure time and temperature.

mixing and attainment of a viscosity of the mixture that precludes its placement is called the pot life.

The pot life of epoxy resins at room temperature may vary from a few minutes to 6 months (ref. 55). No consistent trend in the effect of fillers on the pot life of epoxy resins has been found (ref. 35). The pot life of some resin-hardener systems was materially lengthened by the addition of fillers. In other systems, however, the addition of certain fillers caused shorter pot lives. Data presented by Volk (ref. 1) indicate that increasing the content of a filler which normally increases the pot life of an epoxy will further extend the pot life.

The urethane foam-in-place materials have very short pot lives. Because of their very rapid rates of reaction, frequently less than a minute is available for mixing and pouring the materials (ref. 3).

Flow and Viscosity

Flow and viscosity are related terms that are applied to two different encapsulation techniques. Flow is an empirical quantity, applicable to transfer molding by using the Hull spiral-mold test, which will indicate the molding properties of a material under a given set of test conditions. Viscosity is a fundamental property that is of importance in the casting of embedment materials.

In the Hull spiral-mold test, a mold consisting of a continuous, uniform spiral groove is employed. The material is fed under pressure into the center of the spiral, through which it flows as far as the given test conditions will force it. The total length of the spiral is 100 inches. The test is sensitive to pressure, temperature, and to the characteristics of the material. Spiral flows of a typical low-pressure, high-flow epoxy molding compound at 300° F after a 10-second preheat are: 28 inches at 125 psi, 38 inches at 250 psi, 53 inches at 500 psi, 80 inches at 1000 psi, and 100 inches at 2000 psi (ref. 27). The spiral flow of a typical heat-resistant epoxy under 250 psi at 300° F is 20 inches. The design of the spiral flow mold and the flow test procedure for its use are explained in Epoxy Molding Material Institute Specification EMMI–1.

Low viscosity is desirable in most casting applications since the more fluid materials handle and pour easily, and will penetrate and fill intricate cavities. Optimum viscosities of such materials range from less than 100 centipoises (cp) in some formulations to well over 20 000 cp in more viscous resins. The normal range for casting is 1000 to 5000 cp (ref. 1). The applicable NASA specifications have the following viscosity limitations: for epoxies, 500 poises maximum (50 000 cp); for silicones, 150 to 320 poises maximum, depending on type; polyurethanes, not less than 100 nor more than 300 poises for freshly mixed ingredients from a two-part kit.

Exotherm

The curing reaction of thermosetting resins is always accompanied by the evolution of heat, which causes the temperature of the material to rise above the ambient temperature. The peak temperature above the ambient temperature is called the exotherm (ref. 1). This temperature can be high, and its value and the time to reach it are important.

In large masses of encapsulating compounds, the increases in temperature can be large, and cause excessive curing shrinkage, cracks, and even chemical decomposition indicated by charring. The incorporation of a filler into the compound increases its heat capacity and tends to reduce its exothermic temperature during cure (ref. 35). Volk's explanation (ref. 1) of the effect of filler additions on exotherm is slightly different. Volk reasons that since the heat generated is directly related to the amount of resin polymerized, the addition of chemically inert fillers serves to dilute the resin, thus reducing the volume of resin in a given volume of the filled encapsulating material. Vore (ref. 59) found that the exothermic temperature rise during the cure of Stycast 1090 is 29° F with an oven temperature of 122° F, and 27° F with an oven temperature of 221° F, and is therefore, essentially independent of cure temperature.

Curing Shrinkage

The shrinkage of an embedding material during curing is important in the encapsulation of electronic devices. A material having a large amount of shrinkage during cure may develop high stresses within the embedment and may impose large forces on electrical components and joints.

Shrinkage values are reported in the literature in two different ways. Drinkard and Snyder (ref. 5) report the linear shrinkage in inches/inch; Sperry (ref. 48) and Fischbein and Dichiaro (ref. 60) report volume shrinkage in percent. The shrinkage data compiled by Drinkard and Snyder are shown in figure 14 (ref. 5). In this illustration the NASA specification limits are converted from volume shrinkage to linear shrinkage. Sperry (ref. 48) reports volume shrinkage of solid polyurethane materials as from 2 to 5 percent (linear

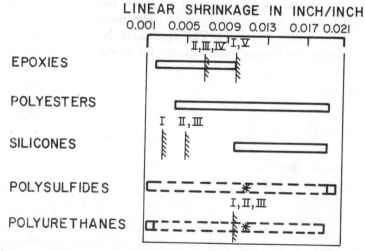

*Under certain conditions, the ranges of these materials may extend as shown

FIGURE 14.—Ranges of typical values of linear shrinkage during cure of embedment materials.

shrinkage of from 0.0067 to 0.017 inch/inch). Fischbein and Dichiaro (ref. 60) report the shrinkage of several commercial adhesives to be in the range of from 2 to 6 percent. The addition of fillers to epoxy encapsulating materials will significantly reduce the curing shrinkage.

OTHER ENVIRONMENTAL FACTORS

In addition to the commonly measured mechanical, thermal, and electrical characteristics of embedment materials, which are discussed above, there are some data on how extreme or unusual environments can affect these materials. This section deals with problems arising from the effects of such phenomena.

Water Absorption

Water absorption of polymers used for electronic module embedment is usually less than 1 percent by weight when it is measured by the standard 24-hour exposure to boiling water. Figure 15 shows ranges of values for the several classes of polymers (ref. 5). Absorptions may be considerably higher in tests of longer duration. Seven-day exposure to water at 25° C of different epoxy/hardener systems containing different mineral fillers (ref. 35) showed that while some fillers decreased water absorption in all cases other fillers increased water absorption with some epoxy curing agents and not with others.

Serious loss of adhesive strength has been reported (ref. 61) for a variety of polymers when they were exposed simultaneously to moisture and mechanical stress. This effect has been confirmed by other investigators for adhesive-bonded aluminum joints exposed to weathering, both stressed and unstressed (refs. 62 and 63). In humid environments adhesion failures at the leads, together with internal stresses present in the embedment material, can create paths by which moisture may reach the embedded circuitry. Particular attention should be given to sealing the module's leads when long-term service in humid environments is anticipated.

Space Environment

The environments encountered in space include high vacuum, high and low extremes of temperature, and electromagnetic radiation. The effects of space environments on polymers used for module embedment have been extensively studied (refs. 49 and 64 through 69), and it has been generally concluded that these materials are serviceable under space conditions for the time periods presently visualized for space missions.

Special attention must be given to conditioning polymers that will be used inside spacecraft or in specialized unmanned satellites, in order

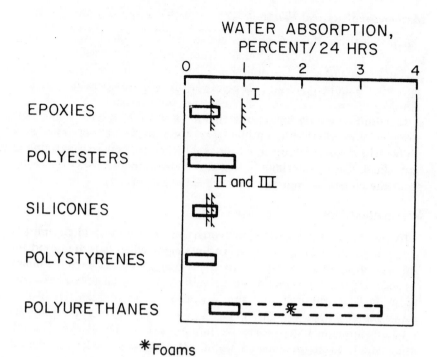

FIGURE 15.—Range of typical values of water absorption.

to eliminate outgassing of unreacted volatile elements of low molecular weight (refs. 46, 70, 71, and 72).

Sterilization

Embedment materials that are resistant to thermal sterilization cycles are becoming increasingly important, particularly for modules intended for use in lunar and interplanetary space probes and surgical implants. The Jet Propulsion Laboratory (JPL), under NASA sponsorship, has had an extensive program underway since 1963 to investigate ways of sterilizing materials and components of spacecraft, including electronic circuitry (refs. 73 through 75). Additional information has been reported by the U.S. Army (ref. 76) and by North American Rockwell Corporation (ref. 77). These investigations indicate that some polymers, including the polyurethanes, degraded and lost their adhesive properties during sterilization, while others, such as the silicones, improved slightly in their strength and electrical properties. Research to develop superior sterilizable silicon-type polymers is being sponsored by NASA (ref. 78).

Mechanical Shock and Vibration

A prime reason for embedding electronic circuit modules is to protect delicate electronic components from mechanical forces. Motorola, in simple tests of such transmissible vibrations as bouncing and shaking (refs. 79 and 80), has determined the effect of temperature on the damping properties of some silicones and polyurethanes, and has also shown that the vibration-transmission spectra of various silicones produced by different manufacturers were markedly different. For embedding telemetry circuits that would be subjected to extremely high shock forces (500 000 g), epoxies were found to be superior to polyesters, silicones, phenolics, and urethanes (ref. 39).

Damage from Products of Decomposition

Garland (ref. 81) has reported corrosion of a number of metals by the products of decomposition in various types of insulating materials. Vapors and extracted materials from polyvinyl chloride were the most corrosive agents that would most readily attack such metals as cadmium, lead, magnesium, and zinc. Polyester, ABS, and diallyl phthalate resins also caused some metal corrosion. Epoxy and polysulfide potting compounds were corrosive to copper. Only slight corrosion of either anodized or unanodized aluminum was caused by any of the polymers studied.

Weigand and Hanna (ref. 82) showed that gaseous products from decomposing styrene-polyester systems, epoxies, and polyimides can combine with oxygen-containing atmospheres to form explosive mixtures in confined places.

CHAPTER 5

Effects of Embedment on Module Functioning

It is well known that embedment causes changes in the electrical values of some circuit components, particularly coils and capacitors (refs. 43, 53, and 83 through 87). These changes are due principally to the mechanical stressing of the components caused by curing shrinkage, and thermal expansion and contraction of the embedment material. The magnitude of the change in electrical properties of components can be used as a measure of the stresses in some cases. The presence of these stresses in embedded circuits is of major concern, not so much because of changes in component values, for which allowances can be made in the component's design, but because the stresses can cause damage to the components and fracture of the circuit interconnections. The latest edition of NASA SP–5002 contains an appendix describing problems presently being encountered with failures of solder joints on conformally coated printed-circuit boards (ref. 88). Although a number of factors apparently contribute to these failures, one of them is the stressing of the solder joints during thermal cycling. This is caused by the conformal coating, which has a coefficient of thermal expansion different from those of the board or the components and, in addition, usually undergoes its glass transition within the range of the thermal cycles. (The glass transition is a phenomenon peculiar to polymers that involves a change in their character from viscous, rubbery materials at temperatures above their glass transition temperatures to hard, brittle materials below their transition temperatures.)

INTERNAL STRESSES IN EMBEDMENT COMPOUNDS

Wallhausser (ref. 89) makes a distinction between processing shrinkage and post-shrinkage of thermosetting plastics. He defines processing shrinkage somewhat arbitrarily as the difference in dimensions between the molded part and the cool mold that is observed after the part has stood for from 24 to 168 hours at 20° C and 65 percent relative humidity. Any dimensional changes that occur

43

beyond this time or as a result of cooling under nonstandard conditions, he calls post-shrinkage.

Wallhausser enumerates five causes for processing shrinkage: Release of moisture from the molding compound, volume reduction by reactions to curing, escape of reaction products with low molecular weight, differences in thermal contraction between the part and the mold during cooling to room temperature, and elastic recoil of the molded material. The causes of post-shrinkage are different, although they may occur simultaneously with those of processing shrinkage. They are largely irreversible and include: Post-curing, release of occluded gases, structural changes in resin and filler, and reorientation of filler particles.

Steele (ref. 90), working with a filled epoxy resin and strain-gage transducers, observed increases in internal compressive stress as high as 11250 psi over a 16-month period following embedment. This was caused by post-curing. Steele also noted that the stresses could not be relieved by thermal treatments (fig. 16). Johnson and Ryan (ref. 85) have also observed an effect in electronic modules that was noted by Wallhausser, that processing shrinkages and the related internal stresses are not isotropic, but are strongly influenced by

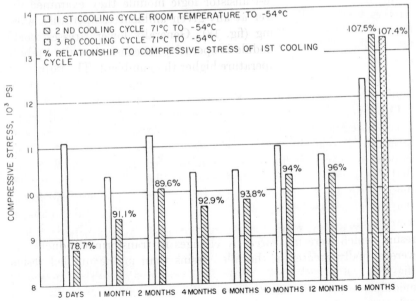

FIGURE 16.—Compressive stress at −54° C of a filled epoxy embedment compound during temperature cycling, measured after various intervals of storage time.

such factors as the shape and position of the mold, processing conditions, and the geometry of the circuitry being embedded.

Stucki, Fuller, and Carpenter (ref. 43), using 0.050-inch diameter toroidal ferrite-core transducers embedded in modules fabricated with epoxy, silicone, and foamed polyurethane embedment materials, have shown that the maximum stresses developed during thermal cycling increase as the embedment material becomes more rigid. As the temperature is decreased, approaching the glass transition, internal stresses begin to rise, reaching a plateau at a temperature somewhat below the glass transition. In figure 17, A and B represent rigid epoxies; C and D are semiflexible epoxies; E is a foamed silicone rubber; and F is a duplex coating. Low temperature stresses as high as 33 000 psi were observed in rigid epoxies. One semiflexible resin investigated had a lower glass transition and a plateau stress of 23 000 psi. Another semiflexible resin showed a maximum stress of only 8000 psi, while a polyurethane foam developed essentially no stress over the entire temperature range from 100° C down to −35° C. It was also found that the addition of a silicone rubber undercoat with the 8000-psi resin had very little effect on the stress detected by the transducer.

By using the microtransducers, the investigators were able to measure stresses at different locations in operable circuit modules. They found that for the diode-transistor logic module they examined the stresses were usually lower at any given ambient temperature when the module was operating (fig. 18). Generally lower stresses would be expected when the module is operating, because then the embedment material sees a temperature higher than ambient. The important result of their investigation was recognition that stress in the more rigid resins is significantly dependent on the temperature.

Lundberg (ref. 86), using a ferrite E-core transformer as his transducer, noted much the same dependence of internal stress on temperature and its relation to the rigidity of materials as Stucki and his associates observed. The most significant finding of Lundberg was that the internal stresses caused by silica fillers assisted in achieving thermal expansion-matching with the embedded circuitry. He found that, although more nearly equal coefficients of thermal expansion were obtained, internal stresses in rigid and semirigid embedment resins, which were measured by changes in transformer inductance, were actually greater in the filled resins than in the unfilled resins (figs. 19 and 20). This effect was attributed to the increase in elastic modulus caused by the filler. Fillers had no effect on transformer inductance when used with the very flexible urethane embedment compounds.

Johnson and Ryan (ref. 85) observed that internal stresses were

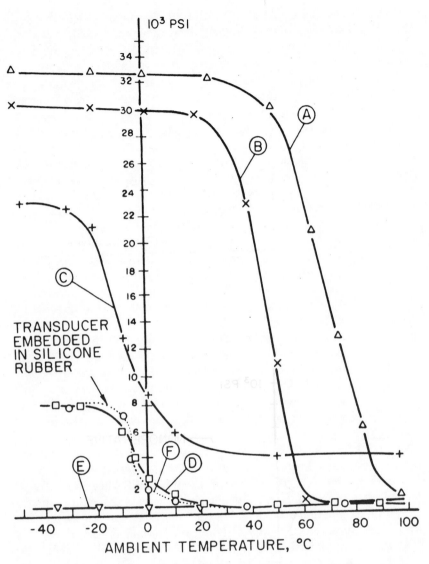

FIGURE 17.—Variation of internal stress in electronic modules with temperature. (Used by permission of *Electronic Production and Packaging*.)

lower than expected (considering rigidity) when they used microsphere-filled embedment compounds. They attributed this to crushing of the layer of microspheres adjacent to the transducers, which acted as capacitors in their investigation.

Dorfman (ref. 91) and Smith (ref. 92) have considered the effects of embedment stresses on welded joints. Dorfman used modules

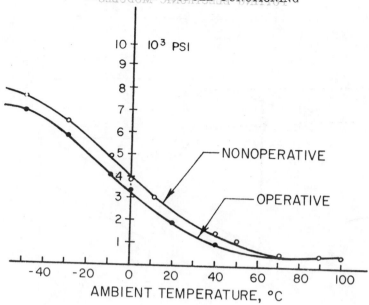

a.

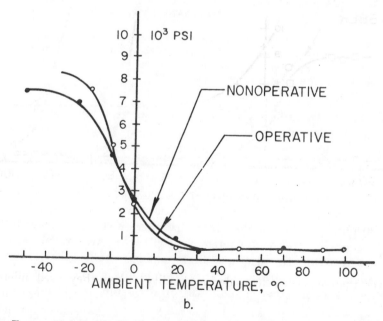

b.

FIGURE 18.—Examples of experimentally measured stresses at different points in a diode-transistor logic module. (Used by permission of *Electronic Production and Packaging*.)

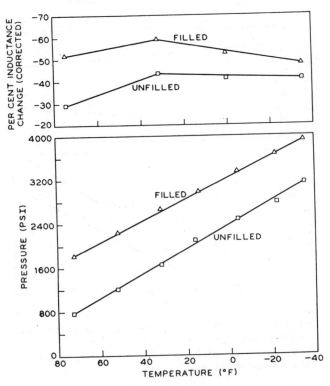

FIGURE 19.—Transducer inductance change as a function of
ambient temperature for rigid epoxies. (Reprinted from
Industrial and Engineering Chemistry by permission of
the American Chemical Society.)

containing a multiplicity of interconnected weld joints having different known strength levels. They showed that stresses sufficient to cause failures in some of the joints were developed during thermal cycling. The largest number of weld failures occurred when an unfilled epoxy resin was used, which may not be consistent with Lundberg's findings. No failures were observed with polyurethane foams, but some failures occurred with filled epoxies even when the filler was microspheres. Dorfman also noted that there was a greater tendency for weld failure when the interconnected welds were widely spaced in the modules. He suggested that reducing the lengths of nickel-ribbon runs in cordwood modules by minimizing the distances between the points they connect will decrease the likelihood of weld failure.

Nikolaychik (ref. 47), apparently following up the investigation by Smith, has presented a detailed analysis of the stress to which a cross-wire weld terminating an axial-lead component is subjected by

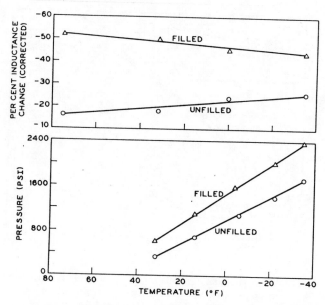

FIGURE 20.—Transducer inductance change as a function of ambient temperature for semirigid epoxies. (Reprinted from *Industrial and Engineering Chemistry* by permission of the American Chemical Society.)

the embedment material during thermal cycling. Strain-gage transducers were used that had been sealed in cylindrical bodies and coated, except for their axial leads, with silicone undercoat to minimize effects of the embedment on the transducer body. Before being embedded, lengths of ribbon were cross-wire welded to the leads. Outputs of the strain gages were converted to loads and plotted. The hysteresis curves in figures 21 and 22 show the variations in load during temperature cycling on the welds of two transducers which were embedded in different commercial epoxies. Curing stresses and their changes with time were also observed. Compressive loads as large as 50 pounds and tensile loads of up to 45 pounds on the axial leads were reported on different transducers. These loads apparently did not cause failures because the welds were in heavier materials that are usually used in module welding (0.040 Ni wire to 0.010 Ni ribbon).

THERMAL DESIGN

The design of modular circuitry is of primary importance in the control of internal stresses. Heat-generating components should be arranged as symmetrically as possible and adequate heat sinks should be provided. The detailed thermal design of modular circuitry is a

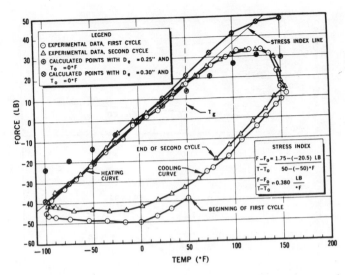

FIGURE 21.—Variation of loads on weld joints as a function of ambient temperature in different embedment materials. Transducer no. 37 in Hysol 4215. (Used by permission of the Society of Automotive Engineers.)

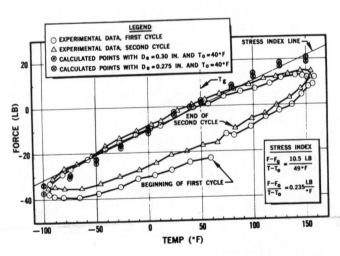

FIGURE 22.—Variation of loads on weld joints as a function of ambient temperature in different embedment materials. Transducer no. 36 in Stycast 1090. (Used by permission of the Society of Automotive Engineers.)

complex subject and references 93 through 98 contain comprehensive discussions of the subject. Failure rates of solid-state components are strong functions of operating temperature, doubling with every 18° C rise (ref. 99). Consequently, reductions of only a few degrees are worthwhile.

Use of internal heat sinks is sometimes sufficient to prevent local hot spots that, in addition to degrading components, can cause local overcuring of the embedment compound. Thermally conductive (metal-filled) cements can be used to assure good thermal contact of the component with the sink. Silicone grease, special grades of which are fairly good thermal conductors without being electrical conductors, should be substituted for the metal-filled cements if there is any danger of shorting the component's leads. In the Nimbus weather satellite, a silica-filled silicone grease, which has a low content of volatile material and a low bleed rate, was used for this purpose (ref. 100).

CHAPTER 6

Production Methods for Embedment

Transistors, silicon integrated circuits, and thin- and thick-film hybrid circuits are now being embedded in plastics on a mass-production basis. Silicon surfaces must be specially protected with passive films prior to embedment. The method of production used in these high-volume applications is transfer molding. The small size of microcircuits does not eliminate the problems, previously discussed, pertaining to older, larger types of circuits. Power densities in microcircuits are often very high, and heat dissipation is a continuing problem. The fragility of leads and interconnection bonds imposes limits on allowable stresses in handling and embedment. References 101 through 106 contain further information on these and other applications of modular embedment, which are now evolving. The remainder of this report will deal with the embedment of cordwood and planar circuit-board modules.

EMBEDMENT PROCEDURE .

Up to about 1964, the established method of module embedment was by casting a pourable resin around the circuitry. Small volumes of production, and the unavailability of small-scale transfer-molding equipment and soft-flow resins appeared to rule out the transfer-molding process, except for a few high-production modules of rugged construction. This situation is now rapidly changing, and transfer molding is replacing casting as the preferred method of embedment. Procedures for transfer molding, however, have not yet been formally documented. Table VI itemizes the pertinent NASA procedures for the embedment of modules, which contain much detailed information on the step-by-step techniques of the embedment process. Because these and other similar documents are readily available, the following discussions will deal principally with recent developments.

CASTING

The casting of liquid resin into an open mold cavity containing the modular circuit is a familiar process in many plants. This process requires large numbers of individual molds and considerable physical space to accommodate the resin-mixing, degassing, mold-assembly,

TABLE VI.—*National Aeronautics and Space Administration procedures related to embedment of electronic modules and connectors*

Specification	Specification title	Date
MSFC–PROC–186C	Potting and Molding Cable Assemblies, Using Elastomeric Compounds, Procedure for.	Sept. 1965.
MSFC–PROC–196B	Potting Cable Assemblies, Using Epoxy Resin Compounds, Procedure for.	Sept. 1965, Amend. Dec. 1965.
MSFC–PROC–257A	Conformal Coating (Epoxy), Application of, Procedure for.	Nov. 1965, Amend. June 1965.
MSFC–PROC–293A	Coating, Conformal, (Polyurethane), Printed Circuit Assemblies, Procedure for.	Nov. 1963, Amend. May 1965.
MSFC–PROC–310	Potting of Electrical Distributors, Procedure for.	Sept. 1963.
MSFC–PROC–380	Potting, Encapsulating and Molding, Using Silicone Rubber, Procedure for.	Jan. 1965, Amend. July 1965.
MSFC–PROC–412	Modules, Electronic, Encapsulating, Procedure for.	March 1965, Amend. Sept. 1965.
MSFC–PROC–442	Use of Formed-in-Place, Polyurethane for Electronic Equipment.	April 1965.
NASA–TM X–50354	Instruction No. 7, Technical Information. Potting Compounds and Sealants by F. N. LeDoux, Goddard Space Flight Center.	Rev. April 1962.

and pouring operations, and also the in-process embedded modules during their curing cycle of several hours. The casting process is well established, however, and is capable of giving excellent results.

It is possible to cast bodies having tolerances as small as ± 0.001 inch if proper attention is given to the resin formulation and to minimizing the exotherm (ref. 107). Satisfactory production-casting tolerances have been achieved using silicone rubber molds (ref. 108), silicone rubber mold faces backed with metal (ref. 103), and plastisol molds (ref. 109). Any of these mold materials offers savings in mold-preparation costs and greater convenience in production than the more common metal molds (fig. 23).

Athough some work has been done with the centrifuging of filled molds as a means of obtaining sound embedments (ref. 110), degassing of the liquid resin by vacuum prior to its use appears to be a much more

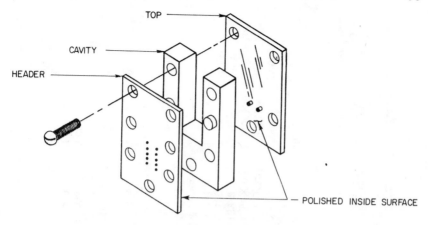

FIGURE 23.—Exploded view of mold for casting embedment materials around electronic circuits.

practical method of eliminating porosity. When casting microsphere-filled resin systems, special care must be taken to ensure that the microspheres are uniformly distributed just prior to pouring, because they tend to separate from the resin. Stirring must be done gently to avoid rupturing the relatively fragile spheres.

TRANSFER MOLDING

Transfer molding is done with gelled, or B-stage resin systems that are in the form either of granular solids or compact preforms. The resin charge is first heated in a cylindrical chamber for a predetermined time, after which it is forced through a suitable channel into a closed mold containing the electronic circuit. Final curing takes place in the mold, but transfer-molding resins are compounded to have very rapid curing times, of the order of seconds to several minutes. Multiple die cavities can be used to produce large numbers of embedded items per shot. The transfer-molding process is described in detail in references 4, 27, 111, and 112. The advantages of transfer molding over casting, as they pertain to production rates and cleanliness of the production area, are at once apparent. There is also evidence (ref. 113) that transfer molding, when used to embed identical modules, can give a better quality embedment than casting.

Transfer-molding embedments of electronic modules were done on a large scale for the Pershing weapon system by the Martin Company (ref. 114). Since that program, Martin has continued to use the technique in research and in production. A recent report (ref. 115) listed measurements of the properties of several commercially available transfer molding compounds (table VII). Outgassing of all of these

TABLE VII.—*Data on transfer-molding compounds*

Test	Method	Pacific resins and chemical 90-B-1	Furane 403-S-3	Furane 8339	Hysol XMG5F E582	Hysol XMG5 E437
Dielectric strength (v/mil)	MIL-I-16923	144.8	417.7	329.1	302.5	304.7
Dielectric constant at 1 kHz	FTMS-406	7.64	6.73	5.43	5.18	5.12
Dissipation factor at 1 kHz	FTMS-406	0.009	0.022	0.010	0.004	0.003
Volume resistivity (Ohm-cm)	MIL-I-16923	4.3×10^{13}	4.3×10^{13}	7.19×10^{13}	7.9×10^{13}	8.63×10^{13}
Surface resistivity (Ohms)	ASTM D257	1.52×10^{13}	1.52×10^{13}	1.52×10^{13}	1.37×10^{13}	1.32×10^{13}
Arc resistance (seconds)	ASTM D495	125.3	182.8	132.3	71.9	99.9
Thermal conductivity (BTU hr/ft/° F) Comparative 50° C		0.194	0.229	0.196	0.144	0.210
Comparative 100°C		0.203	0.236	0.214	0.167	0.221
Fungus resistance	MIL-E-5272	No signs of fungus growth				
Specific gravity	FTMS-406	1.82	1.67	1.60	2.06	1.79
Water absorption (percent)	ASTM D570	0.062	0.073	0.086	0.083	0.100
Thermal shock resistance	MIL-I-16923 Type B cycle	No failures				
Coefficient of linear thermal expansion (in./in. — ° C).	ASTM D696	4.65×10^{-5}	4.51×10^{-5}	4.60×10^{-5}	5.95×10^{-5}	5.37×10^{-5}
Compressive strength (psi)	ASTM D695	20 075	15 500	21 940	20 563	19 570
Flexural strength	ASTM D790	7 042	9 759	11 780	10 600	10 450
Tensile strength	ASTM D638	4 487	5 331	6 036	5 606	4 696
Volume shrinkage (percent)		2 695	2 040	2 959	3 046	2 353
Hardness (Shore D)	FTMS-406	90	90	90	90	90
Flow (inches)	EMMI 1-66	25	34	37	56	28

compounds was reported to be extremely low. Weight losses given are all under 0.003 percent at 10^{-5} torr, but the duration of the outgassing tests was inadvertently omitted from the report.

If a module is to be embedded by transfer molding, care should be taken to ensure uniform and complete filling of the die cavity with a minimum of turbulence. Dead spaces that result in voids should be eliminated. Transfer-molding resins are designed to flow at low pressures during molding, but some forces will inevitably be exerted on the circuitry, which must be able to resist them.

Typical transfer-molding compounds will contain powdered fillers. Compounds with fibrous fillers do not generally flow well. Some work has been done with microsphere-filled transfer-molding compounds with apparent success, despite their fragility (ref. 112).

Molds required for transfer molding are two- or three-piece steel molds, which are often chromium plated for resistance to wear. Some molds are designed so they can be evacuated prior to entry of the resin, but most of them are merely vented. Molds for embedment of electronic modules and components are small and light enough to be inserted into and removed from the molding machine by a single operator, and are usually equipped with insulated handles for this purpose. The problem of mold inventory, which is a serious one in an electronics development laboratory, has largely been overcome by special mold designs that incorporate removable metal inserts to adjust the size and shape of the cavity to one of a number of standard sizes.

The wider availability of laboratory-scale transfer-molding presses, soft-flow embedment resins, and imaginative mold designs, together with the current interest in transfer molding for embedding transistors, integrated circuits, and hybrid microcircuits, will stimulate the use of transfer molding as a routine method of embedding many discrete components in the near future.

REFERENCES

1. VOLK, C.; LEFFORGE, J.; and STETSON, R.: Electrical Encapsulation. Reinhold Publishing Corporation and Chapman & Hall, Ltd., 1962.
2. HARPER, C. A.: Electronic Packaging With Resins, A Practical Guide for Materials and Manufacturing Techniques. McGraw-Hill Book Co., Inc., 1961.
3. HARPER, C. A.: Plastics for Electronics. Kiver Publications, 1964.
4. VAILL, E. W.: Transfer Molding. Modern Plastics Encyclopedia, Vol. 44, No. 1A. McGraw-Hill Book Co., 1966, pp. 746–756.
5. DRINKARD, E. V.; and SNYDER, E. E.: User-Oriented Data Guide to Potting and Encapsulating Compounds. ASD TR 61–297 (AD–290823) American Machine and Foundry Company, Alexandria, Va., June 1960 to June 1961.
6. MERRIGAN, M. A.: Handbook of Design Criteria for Micro-Electronic System Packages. Final Report in 4 vols., RADC–TR–67–125 (AD–655762, AD–655763, AD–655764, AD–655765) Hughes Aircraft Company, Fullerton, Calif., 1967.
7. MILEK, J. T.: Effects of Fillers on the Electrical Properties of Plastics and Elastomer Materials. EPIC IR–58, Hughes Aircraft Company, Culver City, Calif., 1967.
8. MILEK, J. T.: A Survey on Conformal Coatings for Printed Circuit Boards. EPIC IR–46, Hughes Aircraft Company, Culver City, Calif., 1967.
9. MOLZON, A. E.: Encapsulation of Electronic Parts in Plastic—A Review. (AD–648420) Plastics Technical Evaluation Center, Feltman Research Labs., Picatinny Arsenal, Dover, N.J., 1967.
10. BURLEY, C. H.; EASTERDAY, J. L.; and KAISER, D. A.: Industrial Survey of Electronic Packaging. (N67–19037; RSIC–614; AD–647137) Battelle Memorial Institute, Columbus, Ohio, 1966.
11. MILEK, J. T.: A Bibliography on Encapsulation, Embedment, and Potting Compounds. EPIC IR–13, Rev. 2, Hughes Aircraft Company, Culver City, Calif., 1966.
12. KLAPHEKE, J. W.; VEAZIE, W. H.; HOLT, J. C.; and EASTERDAY, J. L.: Electronic Packaging: A Bibliography. (RSIC–534; AD–634004) Battelle Memorial Institute, Columbus, Ohio, 1966.
13. McCORMICK, HELEN B.: Packaging and Interconnections for Miniaturized Electronic Systems: An Annotated Bibliography. (AD–443450) Lockheed Missiles and Space Company, Sunnyvale, Calif., 1963.
14. ANON.: Embedding Materials for Modular Assemblies: A Partially Annotated Bibliography. (AD–403705) Lockheed Missiles and Space Company, Sunnyvale, Calif., 1963.
15. PEARCY, M. M.: High Temperature Materials for Encapsulation: An Annotated Bibliography. SRB–60–13 (AD–248358) Lockheed Aircraft Corporation, 1960.
16. ANON.: Materials and Processes for High-G Gyro Application. (AF 33 (615)–1013) AF Avionics Laboratory, Research and Technology Division, Air Force Systems Command, Wright-Patterson Air Force Base, Ohio, 1965.

17. VONDRACEK, C. H.: An Evaluation of Inorganic Potting Compounds. Research Paper 64–131–342–P2, Research Laboratories, Westinghouse Electric Corporation, Pittsburgh, Pa., 1964.

18. HILLHOUSE, R. T.: Cementitious Ceramic Materials. PA–TM–1204 (AD–414515) Plastics Technical Evaluation Center, Feltman Research Labs., Picatinny Arsenal, Dover, N.J., 1963.

19. CUMING, W. R.: Ceramic Encapsulants. Electronic Design, vol. 8, May 25, 1960, pp. 54, 55.

20. WILSON, G. R.; ET AL.: High Temperature Dielectric Liquid Materials for Potting of Electronic Components. (AD–256759) Monsanto Chemical Company, 1960.

21. FREEMAN, R. E.: Reliability Improvement Through Stabilized Environments. National Electronic Packaging and Production Conference, Long Beach, Calif., Jan. 31–Feb. 2, 1967, and New York, N.Y., June 13–15, 1967, Proceedings of the Technical Program, Conference Sponsored by the Electronic Production and Packaging magazine, Chicago, Ill., 1967, pp. 565–582.

22. ANON.: Alumina Powders Used for Potting. J. Franklin Institute, vol. 269, Feb. 1960, pp. 160, 161.

23. ANON.: Fibrous Potassium Titanate for Insulating and Other Uses to 1204° C. Insulation, vol. 6, Sept. 1960, p. 76.

24. HARPER, C. A.: Resins for Embedding Microelectronic Devices. IEEE Transactions on Component Parts, vol. CP–11, no. 1, March 1964, pp. 22–27.

25. HARPER, C. A.: Embedding Processes and Materials. Machine Design, vol. 38, June 9, 1966, pp. 150–173.

26. LeDOUX, FRANCIS N.: Encapsulation, Electronics, Eccofoam. (N66–17232) Goddard Space Flight Center, Greenbelt, Md., Nov. 1965.

27. DELMONTE, J.: Epoxy Molding Compounds: Materials, Molding and Applications. Insulation, vol. 13, Feb. 1967, pp. 59–63.

28. CRESSY, K.; and McKINNEY, R.: New Materials for Urethane Encapsulation. National Electronic Packaging and Production Conference, Long Beach, Calif., Jan. 31–Feb. 2, 1967, and New York, N.Y., June 13–15, 1967, Proceedings of the Technical Program, Conference Sponsored by the Electronic Production and Packaging magazine, Chicago, Ill., 1967, pp. 363–366.

29. DELMONTE, J.: Liquid Urethane Elastomers as Encapsulating Compounds. Insulation, vol. 10, Oct. 1964, pp. 23–26.

30. MODIC, F. J.: New Fast Curing Silicone Polymers for Electrical and Electronic Uses. Proceedings of the Sixth Electrical Insulation Conference, New York, N.Y., Sept. 13–16, 1965, Conference Sponsored by IEEE, NEMA, and Navy Bureau of Ships, 1965, pp. 131–134.

31. PATTERSON, W. J.: Development of Polymeric Materials for Potting and Encapsulating Electronic Assemblies. NASA TM X–53390, 1966.

32. SCHROEDER, H. A.; ET AL.: SiB Polymer Development. (AD–632035) Chemicals Division, Olin Mathieson Chemical Corp., New Haven, Conn., 1966.

33. BERGEY, R.; SHANTA, C.; and DALPHONE, L.: Results of Potting Compound Filler Investigation. (AD–409329) Great Valley Labs., Burroughs Corporation, Paoli, Pa., 1962.

34. HARPER, C. A.: Thermally Conductive Cast-Resin Compounds for Heat Dissipation. Electro-Technology, vol. 67, no. 4, Apr. 1961, p. 148.

35. ANON.: Comparative Properties of Filled Epoxy Electrical Potting Com-

pounds. Special Report, Chemical and Plastics Division, Union Carbide Corporation, Bound Brook, N.J., Aug. 1959.

36. BAKER, E. C.: Electronic Encapsulant Thermal Conductivities Extended an Order of Magnitude. Electronic Packaging and Production, vol. 6, May 1966, pp. 180–182, 184, 186.

37. ANON.: Manufacturer's literature on BERLON encapsulants. National Beryllia Corporation, Haskell, N.J.

38. QUANT, A. J.: A Low-Density Potting Compound. SCR–417A(N63–83321) Sandia Corporation, Albuquerque, N. Mex., 1961.

39. YOUNG, R. P.: An Examination of Epoxy Systems Useful in Packaging High G Radio Telemeters. AEDC–TDR 62–58(AD–273681) Arnold Air Force Station, Tenn., 1962.

40. LeFAVE, G. M.; GAMERO, R.; and ANGELONI, D. J.: A New concept— Low-Density Elastomer for Missile and Space Systems. Vol. 2 of the Proceedings of the Sixth National Symposium on Materials for Space Vehicle Use, Seattle, Wash., Nov. 18–20, 1963, Symposium Sponsored by Society of Aerospace Material and Process Engineers.

41. STEINHARDT, I. J.; VADOPALAS, P.; and PLUTCHOK, H.: Performance of Fillers at Microwave Frequencies. Proceedings of the Sixth Electrical Insulation Conference, New York, N.Y., Sept. 13–16, 1965, Conference Sponsored by IEEE, NEMA, and Navy Bureau of Ships, 1965, pp. 3–6.

42. HARPER, C. A.: Foams and Low Density Compounds. Insulation, vol. 7, May 1961, pp. 34–41.

43. STUCKI, F. F.; FULLER, W. D.; and CARPENTER, R. D.: Internal Stress Measurement of Encapsulated Electronic Modules. Electronic Packaging and Production, vol. 7, Feb. 1967, pp. 39–46.

44. STEIGERWALD, R. M.: Lightweight, Soluble Encapsulating Compound Permits Repair of Electronics. Insulation, vol. 10, no. 2, Feb. 1964, pp. 35–38.

45. DUNAETZ, R. A.; and TUCKERMAN, A. J.: Selection and Evaluation of Organic Dielectric Materials for Spacecraft. SAMPE J. (Society of Aerospace Material and Process Engineers Journal), vol. 3, no. 6, Oct./Nov. 1967.

46. STEFANSKI, S. G.: A Guide to Tests for Molding Compounds Used for Aerospace Electronic Components. Insulation, vol. 9, no. 1, Jan. 1963, pp. 22–25.

47. NIKOLAYCHIK, G.: Thermal Stress Analysis of Epoxy Encapsulants. Proceedings of SAE Sponsored Electronic Packaging Conference, New York, N.Y., Feb. 14–16, 1967, pp. 105–125.

48. ANON.: Final Report—Evaluation Testing of Polyurethane Potting Compounds. Rept. No. EJ–330–0548 (AD–431464), Sperry Utah Company, 1963.

49. DE DAPPER, J. W.: Evaluation of Critical Properties of Selected Materials for Electronic Packaging Purposes. (NAS7–100) Jet Propulsion Laboratory, Calif. Inst. of Tech., Pasadena, Aug. 1, 1962.

50. HOLZBAUER, C. R.; and HOLBROOK, R. J.: Foam-in-Place Materials for High Voltage Insulation in a Space Environment. NASA CR–72100, 1967.

51. CHRISTENSEN, D. F.: Environmental Evaluation Data for Silicone Encapsulants. Electrical Manufacturing, vol. 66, no. 1, July 1960, pp. 117–120.

52. ANON.: Electrical Potting Compounds—Surface and Volume Resistivity at Elevated Temperatures for Protracted Times (Phase I: Physical Tests). Rept. 9353, ser. no. 19 (AD–295533) McDonnell Aircraft Corporation, 1963.

53. HARPER, C. A.: Embedding Resin Effects on Components and Circuits. Electronic Packaging and Production, vol. 5, no. 5, May 1965, pp. 71–78.

54. GALE, E.: Device for Measuring Thermal Conductivity of Potting Compounds. (AD–415501) Technical Information Series, Light Military Electronics Dept., General Electric Company, Utica, N.Y., Apr. 10, 1961.

55. ANON.: Properties of Encapsulating Compounds. Electronic Products, vol. 5, no. 11, Apr. 1963, pp. 46–55.

56. HARPER, C. A.: Electrical Insulating Materials. Machine Design, vol. 39, no. 23, Sept. 28, 1967, pp. 134–162.

57. ANON.: Electrical Potting Compounds—Surface and Volume Resistivity at Elevated Temperatures for Protracted Times (Phase II: Electrical Tests). Rept. 9354, ser. no. 18 (AD–295538) McDonnell Aircraft Corporation, 1963.

58. OLYPHANT, M., JR.: Effects of Cure and Aging on Dielectric Properties. Proceedings of the Sixth Electrical Insulation Conference, New York, N.Y., Sept. 13–16, 1965, Conference Sponsored by IEEE, NEMA, and Navy Bureau of Ships, 1965, pp. 12–19.

59. VORE, E.: ESP Test for Maximum Exothermic Temperature Developed by Stycast 1090 Epoxy Potting Compound During Potting of Cordwood Modules. Rept. No. TM–756 (AD–439541) Military Electronics Division, Motorola, Inc., Scottsdale, Ariz., 1963.

60. FISCHBEIN, R. A.; and DICHIARO, J. V.: Determination of the Shrinkage of Adhesives During Cure. AEC Research and Development Report, Monsanto Research Corporation, Jan. 20, 1967.

61. SHARP, L. H.: Some Aspects of the Permanence of Adhesive Joints. Structural Adhesive Bonding. Vol. III of Applied Polymer Symposia, M. J. Bodmar, ed., Interscience Publishers, 1966.

62. WEGMAN, R. F.; ET AL.: How Weathering and Aging Affect Bonded Aluminum. Adhesives Age, vol. 10, no. 10, Oct. 1967, pp. 22–26.

63. CARTER, G. F.: Outdoor Durability of Adhesive Joints Under Stress. Adhesives Age, vol. 10, no. 10, Oct. 1967, pp. 32–37.

64. MATTICE, J. J.: The Vacuum-Thermal Stability of Organic Coating Materials. Part I. The Polyurethanes. WADD 60–126 (AD–245327) Wright-Patterson Air Force Base, Ohio, 1960.

65. BROADWAY, N. J.; KING, R. W.; and PALINCHAK, S.: Space Environmental Effects on Materials and Components. Vol. I, Elastomeric and Plastic Materials. Appendix G: Potting Compounds. RSIC 150–Vol. 1 (AD–603371) Battelle Memorial Institute, Columbus, Ohio, 1964.

66. THORNE, J. A.; WHIPPLE, C. L.; and BOEHM, A. B.: Space Environmental Effects on Silicone Insulating Materials. Proceedings of the Sixth Electrical Insulation Conference, New York, N. Y., Sept. 13–16, 1965, Conference Sponsored by IEEE, NEMA, and Navy Bureau of Ships, 1965, pp. 219–223.

67. KERLIN, E. E.: Measured Effects of the Various Combinations of Nuclear Radiation, Vacuum, and Cryotemperatures on Engineering Materials— Annual Report. Vol. I, Radiation-Vacuum and Radiation-Vacuum Cryotemperature Tests. (NAS8–2450) General Dynamics, Fort Worth, Texas, May 1, 1964.

68. KERLIN, E. E.: Measured Effects of the Various Combinations of Nuclear Radiation, Vacuum, and Cryotemperatures on Engineering Materials— Biennial Report for the period May 1, 1964, to May 1, 1966. (NAS8–1450) General Dynamics, Fort Worth, Texas, July 1, 1966.

69. THOMAS, J. P.; and STOUT, R. J.: Effects of Elevated Temperatures and

Reduced Atmospheric Pressure on Adhesives, Potting Compounds and Sealants. ERR-FW-129 (AD-285488) General Dynamics, Fort Worth, Texas, 1962.

70. LYMAN, D. J.: Development of Material Specifications and Qualifications of Polymeric Materials for the JPL Spacecraft Materials Guidebook. NASA CR-75297, 1965.

71. BLACK, J. A.; LYMAN, D. J.; and PARKINSON, D. B.: Development of Material Specifications and Qualifications of Polymeric Materials for the JPL Spacecraft Materials Guidebook. II: RTV Silicone Adhesives and Potting Compounds. NASA CR-64208, 1965.

72. MURACA, R. F.; ET AL. Polymers for Spacecraft Hardware Materials Specifications and Engineering Information. NASA CR-74688, 1966.

73. KOHORST, D. P.; and HARVEY, H.: Polymers for Use in Sterilized Spacecraft. NASA SP-108, 1965. ·

74. FITAK, A. G.; MICHAL, L. M.; and HOLTZE, R. F.: Sterilizable Electronic Packaging, Connectors, Wires, and Cabling Accessories. NASA SP-108, 1965.

75. VISSER, J.: Current Results of the Electronic Part Sterilization Program at the Jet Propulsion Laboratory. Proceedings of the Symposium on Reliability, Sponsored by the Institute of Electrical and Electronics Engineers, the Institute of Environmental Sciences, the Society for Nondestructive Testing, and the American Society for Quality Control, Washington, D.C., Jan. 10-12, 1967.

76. ANON.: Use of Sporicides and Heat to Sterilize Resins, U.S. Army Chemical Corps, Protection Branch, Report of Test No. 4-64, Sept. 16, 1963.

77. LEE, S. M.; LICARI, J. J.; and FEWELL, R. O.: Sterilization Effects on Microelectronics. National Electronic Packaging and Production Conference, Long Beach, Calif., Jan. 31-Feb. 2, 1967, and New York, N.Y., June 13-15, 1967, Proceedings of the Technical Program, Conference Sponsored by the Electronic Production and Packaging magazine, Chicago, Ill., 1967, pp. 583-597.

78. BUTLER, J. M.; and WEBSTER, J. H.: Development of Improved Potting and Encapsulating Compounds for Space Applications. First Annual Summary Report (NAS8-20402) Monsanto Research Corporation, June 17, 1966, to June 16, 1967.

79. ANON.: Comparison of Damping Properties (Bounce) at 25° C, −55° C and 125° C of Eight Flexible Encapsulating Materials. TM-626 (LD) (AD-271207) Military Electronics Division, Motorola, Inc., Scottsdale, Ariz., 1961.

80. ANON.: Comparative Vibration Tests between Westinghouse M #6766-2, General Electric SR-601, and Dow Corning RTV-881. TM-588(LD) (AD-271206) Military Electronics Division, Motorola, Inc., Scottsdale, Ariz., 1961.

81. GARLAND, W. F.: Effect of Decomposition Products from Electrical Insulation on Metal and Metal Finishes. Proceedings of the Sixth Electrical Insulation Conference, New York, N.Y., Sept. 13-16, 1965, Conference Sponsored by IEEE, NEMA, and Navy Bureau of Ships, 1965, pp. 56-60.

82. WEIGAND, B. L.; and HANNA, J. E.: Evaluation of Explosive Hazard of Gases Generated by Transformer Potting Materials When Subjected to Electrical Overloads. Proceedings of the Sixth Electrical Insulation Conference, New York, N.Y., Sept. 13-16, 1965, Conference Sponsored by IEEE, NEMA, and Navy Bureau of Ships, 1965, pp. 9-11.

83. CAMPBELL, E. P.: The Effects of Encapsulation on Electronic Components. Electronic Engineering, vol. 32, June 1960, pp. 366–371.

84. ANON.: Comparative Test of Three Potting Compounds and Four Adhesives Used in the Fabrication of 36 RF Transformers When Bonded to a Gold Plated Chassis. TM No.–801 (AD–447352) Military Electronics Division, Motorola, Inc., Scottsdale, Ariz., 1963.

85. JOHNSON, L. I.; and RYAN, R. J.: Encapsulated Component Stress Testing. Proceedings of the Sixth Electrical Insulation Conference, New York, N.Y., Sept. 13–16, 1965, Conference Sponsored by IEEE, NEMA and Navy Bureau of Ships, 1965, pp. 11–15.

86. LUNDBERG, C. V.: Correlation of Shrinkage Pressures Developed in Epoxy, Polyurethane, and Silicone Casting Resins With Inductance Measurements on Embedded Electronic Components. Paper presented at the 152nd National Meeting, Am. Chem. Soc. (New York), Sept. 11–16, 1966, Industrial and Engineering Chemistry, Product Research and Development, vol. 6, June 1967, pp. 92–100.

87. ARNETT, J. C.: Component Stresses in MO21 Potted Modules. Rept. No. ME–630 (AD–457679) Martin Marietta Corp., Denver, Colo.

88. ANON.: Soldering Electrical Connections—A Handbook. Fourth ed. NASA SP–5002, 1967.

89. WALLHÄUSSER, H.: The Dimensional Stability of Mouldings Obtained from Curable Compounds. Kunststoffe, vol. 55, Jan. 1965, pp. 33–39.

90. STEELE, D. V.: Internal Stresses Developed in an Epoxy Resin Potting Compound During Long Term Storage. (AD–411514) Chemistry Research Division, Naval Ordnance Laboratory, White Oak, Md., 1962.

91. DORFMAN, H.: Weld Stress Evaluation—Electronic Modules. Proceedings of the SAE Sponsored Electronic Packaging Conference, Los Angeles, Calif., Oct. 20–21, 1965, pp. 49–53.

92. SMITH, M. H.: Measurement of Embedment Stresses in Electronic Modules. (NAS7–101) National Electronic Packaging and Production Conference, New York, June 21–23, 1966, Proceedings of the Technical Program, Chicago, Industrial and Scientific Conference Management, Inc., 1966, pp. 427–438.

93. SACRAMONE, P.: An Approach to Space Electronics Thermal Design. National Electronic Packaging and Production Conference, Long Beach, Calif., Jan. 31–Feb. 2, 1967, and New York, N.Y., June 13–15, 1967, Proceedings of the Technical Program, Conference Sponsored by the Electronic Production and Packaging magazine, Chicago, Ill., 1967, pp. 18–42.

94. SNOGRAN, R. C.: Removing Heat from High-Density Packaged Electronics. Paper 67–DE–47, Presented at the American Society of Mechanical Engineers, Design Engineering Conference and Show (New York), May 15–18, 1967.

95. CASAZZA, S. A.: Transient Thermal Analysis of Complex Electronic Assemblies. (DA–19–020–AMC–0215) (Z) Missile Systems Division, Bedford Laboratories, Raytheon Company, Bedford, Mass. Presented at the 22d National Electronics Conference (Chicago, Ill.), Oct. 3–5, 1966, Proceedings of the Conference Sponsored by the Illinois Institute of Technology, the Institute of Electrical and Electronics Engineers Region IV, Northwestern University, and the University of Illinois, Chicago, 1966, pp. 159–164.

96. ADELBERG, M.; and BAKER, E. C.: Thermal Design of Electronic Packages. Paper 65–WA/HT–44, Presented at the Annual Winter Meeting of ASME (Chicago, Ill.), Nov. 7–11, 1965.

97. WELSH, J. P.: Thermal Design of Miniaturized Electronic Equipment. Paper 63–MD–5, Presented at the ASME, Design Engineering Conference and Show (New York), May 20–23, 1963.

98. HRYCAK, P.; ET AL.: The Spacecraft Structure and Thermal Design Considerations. Bell System Technical J., vol. 42, part 1, July 1963, pp. 973–1005.

99. GONZALES, J. I.; and WAUGH, C. E.: Thermal· Characteristics of Potted Electronic Modules. Ultrasonics Engineering, vol. 10, pp. 105–119.

100. LONDON, A.: Thermal Considerations for Electronics Packaging of the Nimbus Spacecraft Control System. National Electronic Packaging and Production Conference, Long Beach, Calif., Jan. 31–Feb. 2, 1967, and New York, N.Y., June 13–15, 1967, Proceedings of the Technical Program, Conference Sponsored by the Electronic Production and Packaging magazine, Chicago, Ill., 1967, pp. 1–17.

101. BEADLES, R. L.: Integrated Silicon Device Technology, vol. XIV. Interconnections and Encapsulation. (AD–654630) Technical Rept. for Jan. 1966 to March 1967, Research Triangle Institute, Durham, N. C., 1967.

102. CAREY, J. P.: Encapsulation of Thick-Film Substrates. National Electronic Packaging and Production Conference, Long Beach, Calif., Jan. 31–Feb. 2, 1967, and New York, N.Y., June 13–15, 1967, Proceedings of the Technical Program, Conference Sponsored by the Electronic Production and Packaging magazine, Chicago, Ill., 1967, pp. 549–557.

103. EVERETT, P. N.: Lead Attachment and Encapsulation Techniques for Thin Film Microcircuits. (AD–611752) Mitre Corporation, Bedford, Mass., 1965.

104. LOCKHART, F. J.: The Role of Silicone Packaging Materials in the Semiconductor Industry. National Electronic Packaging and Production Conference, Long Beach, Calif., Jan. 31–Feb. 2, 1967, and New York, N.Y., June 13–15, 1967, Proceedings of the Technical Program, Conference Sponsored by the Electronic Production and Packaging magazine, Chicago, Ill., 1967, pp. 355–362.

105. LEDOUX, F. N.: Handling, Cleaning, Decontamination and Encapsulation of Mosfets Circuitry. NASA TM X–55338, 1965.

106. HAMBURGER, T.; and GOURSE, S.: Microelectronic Packaging Concepts. (AD–619444) Prepared by Westinghouse Electric Corporation for Rome Air Development Center, Jan. 1, 1964 to Dec. 31, 1964.

107. NELSON, B. W.; MORRISSEY, E. J.; and MARCEY, S. D.: Casting to Close Tolerances with Unfilled Epoxy Resins. Soc. of Plastics Engineers J. vol. 17, March 1961, pp. 257–259.

108. ANON.: Improved Fabrication of Molds for Potting Modules. (AD–444889) Minuteman Producibility Study 078, Central Manufacturing Engineering, 1962.

109. ANON.: Molding Precision Microballoon-Filled Epoxy Parts in Plastisol Molds. (SC–TM–65–462) Manufacturing Process Development Div., Sandia Corporation, 1965.

110. DORFMAN, H.: Encapsulation of Welded Modules. Rept. MRI 270.02 (AD–285736) Lockheed Aircraft Corporation, Missiles and Space Division, Sunnyvale, Calif., 1961.

111. ZECHER, R. F.: Transfer Molding of New Thermoset Compounds. Soc. of Plastics Engineers J., vol. 20, Jan. 1964.

112. HULL, J. L.: Latest Techniques and Equipment for High-Production Encapsulation of Electronic Parts. Proceedings of the Sixth Electrical

Insulation Conference, New York, N.Y., Sept. 13–16, 1965, Conference Sponsored by IEEE, NEMA, and Navy Bureau of Ships, 1965.

113. BUBNEKOVICH, J. R.: A Value Analysis Study Summary Report on Dip Solder vs. Welded Joints. IDEP 347.70.00.00–D3–01 (AD–459816) Great Valley Laboratories, Burroughs Corporation, Paoli, Pa., 1963.

114. UGLIONE, H. L., JR.; and BELL, A. R., JR.: Transfer Molding of High-Density Modules for the Pershing Weapon System. Proceedings of the Western Electronic Show and Convention, San Francisco, Calif., Aug. 24–27, 1965, Technical Papers, Part 1–Military Electronics, North Hollywood, Calif.

115. YATES, G. D.: Establishment of Standards for Compatibility of Printed Circuit and Component Lead Materials. (NAS8–20390) Final Rept., Prepared for Marshall Space Flight Center, Huntsville Ala. by Martin Marietta Corporation, Orlando, Fla., Aug. 1967.

U. S. GOVERNMENT PRINTING OFFICE : 1970 O - 369-147

NATIONAL AERONAUTICS AND SPACE ADMINISTRATION
WASHINGTON, D. C. 20546

OFFICIAL BUSINESS

FIRST CLASS MAIL

```
09U 001 25    35 5FU          70013  00508
IOWA STATE UNIVERSITY OF SCIENCE & TECHNC
AMES, IOWA 50010
```

ATT LIBRARY

*"The aeronautical and space activities of the United States shall
be conducted so as to contribute . . . to the expansion of human
knowledge of phenomena in the atmosphere and space. The
Administration shall provide for the widest practicable and
appropriate dissemination of information concerning its activities
and the results thereof."*

— NATIONAL AERONAUTICS AND SPACE ACT OF 1958

NASA TECHNOLOGY UTILIZATION PUBLICATIONS

These describe science or technology derived from NASA's activities that may be of
particular interest in commercial and other non-aerospace applications.
Publications include:

TECH BRIEFS: Single-page descriptions
of individual innovations, devices,
methods, or concepts.

TECHNOLOGY SURVEYS: Selected
surveys of NASA contributions to
entire areas of technology.

OTHER TU PUBLICATIONS: These
include handbooks, reports, notes,
conference proceedings, special studies,
and selected bibliographies.

*Details on the availability of these
publications may be obtained from:*

National Aeronautics and
Space Administration
Code UT
Washington, D.C. 20546

Technology Utilization publications are
part of NASA's formal series of scientific
and technical publications. Others
include Technical Reports, Technical
Notes, Technical Memorandums,
Contractor Reports, Technical Transla-
tions, and Special Publications.

*Details on their availability
may be obtained from:*

National Aeronautics and
Space Administration
Code US
Washington, D.C. 20546

NATIONAL AERONAUTICS AND SPACE ADMINISTRATION
Washington, D.C. 20546